"The Face of All the World is Changed."

VII

The face of all the world is changed, I think,
Since first I heard the footsteps of thy soul
Move still, oh, still, beside me, as they stole
Betwixt me and the dreadful outer brink
Of obvious death, where I, who thought to sink,
Was caught up into love, and taught the whole
Of life in a new rhythm. The cup of dole
God gave for baptism, I am fain to drink,
And praise its sweetness, Sweet, with thee anear.
The names of country, heaven, are changed away
For where thou art or shalt be, there or here;
And this. .this lute and song. .loved yesterday,
(The singing angels know) are only dear,
Because thy name moves right in what they say.

"Sonnets from the Portuguese"
by Elizabeth Barrett Browning

"The Face of All the World is Changed."

An Autobiographical Study with the Focus on Stuttering.

Ida E. Whitten

"Therapies Used for Stuttering: A Report of the Author's own Case," by Ida
E. Whitten. *The Quarterly Journal of Speech,* Volume XXIV, April 1938.

Printed by Scott Zoller
224 E. Eighth Street
Cincinnati, Ohio 45202

Dedicated to the memory of

DR. SMILEY BLANTON

"In the deeper levels of the mind there are resources of power, strength and courage hardly imagined. *To each person himself is given the task of tapping these levels*, with what assistance he can muster. There are, fortunately, untold resources in each of us if we will only find and utilize them."

Love or Perish, 1955.

CONTENTS

Less anxiety on the Grandpa farm. A new Ford car. Read literary novels. Recited poems before my mirror with no stuttering. Did not see or hear the birds. Heard the woodpecker. Did see the wrens. The sound when a wagon crossed the iron-bridge. My chum, Mary. I learned to concentrate.

I wanted to be in that contest. Practiced poems my mother used for projecting her voice. My stuttering was so my mother thought I could not be in the contest. I had persevered and learned to be an excellent shot with my brother's rifle. I practiced in our barn and in the big, empty barn where I roomed. To fill a barn with sound I learned to speak in a different way. If this were a play, this contest gives the first indication of how the play will end. Why did I want to be in that contest? My father promised me a ring if I won. No sound amplification system. I won first place and second in the county contest. Father gave me a lovely small opal ring which I still wear. I invited our class to our farm for the class picnic, but they wanted a formal picnic area.

No plans for the future. Father got a school for me in a German neighborhood. Studied for the teachers examination to get a certificate so I could teach. The next spring father found a school for me a little nearer home. Footstools and hot lunches. My speech was no problem. A spell of rheumatism, later a gall stone attack. I wanted to go to college.

Stayed with friends of our family and attended the University of Nebraska for two years. Stuttered severely. A cousin's reaction. Won honors in English and archery. Significance of hot lunches and winning in archery. Story of Mary's stutter. My parents moved to Phillipsburg. After two years at the University I taught English at Imperial, Nebraska. There I was more a part of a social group. Back to the University to finish my degree. Anna's humming-bird. Marking time. Taught one year at a small school near Lincoln, then to teach English in the college at Aberdeen, S.D. After two years my stutter became more pronounced. My brother drove up to take me home by way of the Black Hills. We camped in a field where the army worms had taken everything. The healing of home.

Chapter 10. A DIFFERENT MIND SET.   109

Dr. Travis found I should be left-handed. On the trip to Iowa I bought an attractive dress with jacket. Worked toward a master's degree in English Literature at Nebraska. Secured the names of important speech pathologists from the head of the Speech Department. Decided to attend Dr. Blanton's Summer School in Massachusetts. It was a splendid summer. Learned a little about relaxation. Work with Dr. Blanton opened a new world of thought for me. "Muscle tensions." One dream showed a strong attach-ment to my father. No longer remember my dreams. Taught in small school near enough I could be home weekends with my parents. At Thanksgiving attended the annual meeting of ASHA in St. Louis. The next winter I was back at Nebraska and finished my M.A. Degree. Worked in Dr. Blanton's Summer School two summers. 1934–35 I was back at Nebraska. Took psychology courses and read English papers for an English professor. "The sorrow of my predicament." I faced the reality of the situation. I must find help for my speech.

Racine. Picnics. Black Hills. Spotty. Retired from Racine. Father not so well. Passed away. Visited the Suttons in England and drove a rented car around Wales. Algoma on the Lake. Special education study in Lunt, Sweden. Pneumonia in Amsterdam. Spent winter in Phillipsburg. 50th Anniversary of my H.S. Class. Tour of Spain with week in Morocco. Parts of next two winters with the Beckers in Glendale, California. Winter of 1972–73 in Kansas. Diarrhea. Moved to San Diego.

Roses and Gardenias in my yard. Fuchsia baskets. Birds. Sunrise Semester. How did I happen to make the choices that enabled me to have practically perfect speech.

PREFACE

THE SPRING of my retirement from the public schools of Racine, Wisconsin, Dr. Van Riper of Kalamazoo, Michigan, sent a tape. Dr. Van, as we affectionately call him, spoke of himself and of me as being "laborers in the vineyard." On that tape he said I should write a book. This is hardly what he envisaged, but I have long felt I should write something that might illuminate how it came about that I was able to get my stuttering under enough control that I could have a successful professional life; also something that might be a guiding light for some fellow stutterers, their families and friends; something that might aid speech pathologists to better understand stutterers and what stuttering is.

A contemporary Russian writer has this sentence in his introduction, "...the writer merely follows a voice, which dictates the manuscript to him." This is literally what I have done—let an inner voice dictate my story. That is why it has taken me more than eight years to work out this account; it requires time and concentration to understand what that "inner voice" is dictating.

It would seem the incidents, the happenings that an

individual remembers may be some of the ones that influence him most. No doubt some significant memories, on the other hand, that are too painful and threatening to be faced, may be pushed into the unconscious and seemingly forgotten. I pondered, reflected, meditated and thought back. It must be something within me, something the circumstances of life had developed in me that enabled me to persist and never give up or even be discouraged until I found a practical, dependable, comfortable, objective way of managing my speech problem. So I have undertaken an autobiography around my stuttering. So far as I can determine I am the only woman to write in depth of her own stuttering, and I seem to be the only person to write of more than eighty-six years of stuttering.

I am the sum-total of what the events of life made me, together with the physical characteristics I inherited from my parents, and the effects of our rather isolated life on the prairie. Also there were my daydreams. For some years I went along with my stuttering as an inevitable part of my life, until I could no longer endure the drastic limitations and restrictions it was imposing on my future. Then I sought help. Some wise person said it is not the stuttering that matters, but the important thing is the way one deals with it. The way life shaped me determined how I could deal with my speech problem later in life.

These past few retirement years as I meditated and thought back over my life I gradually became aware of the significance of my daydreams. Before that I seem to have considered them just a normal part of life. I was not even much aware that they made up a kind of fantasy life. These daydreams may have begun quite early, before I learned to read, for even though I was dearly loved I

xvi

was a lonely child on our rather isolated farm in north-western Kansas. For such areas that was long before the time of libraries with their magnificent array of beautiful and educational books for children of all ages including pre-schoolers. As soon as I learned to read I made up daydream-stories patterned on the scenes and incidents in the books I read. My stuttering and our somewhat isolated life left me a hurt and lonely young person, but in a different light I was a happy carefree child and young woman. My daydreams were a most marvelous and enchanting escape from the ordinariness of our lives, from the isolation and from the sensitivity associated with my stuttering. My imagination might range over the entire world so far as I knew it. It is known that many stutterers have suicidal thoughts, but I never did. It seems my subconscious mind was able to channel any depressive and threatening feelings of fear and inadequacy into happy daydream-diversions.

Thinking back over the years is rewarding in many ways, but sometimes painful. I came to realize I almost unconsciously turn to some note of joy, of gaiety to relieve the intensity of my feeling. In this story after months of reflecting, studying and writing I finally came to realize that immediately after mention of a sensitive or painful part there is an intrusion of some memory or incident that tends to relieve my own pain and tension. The first instance of this is in Chapter 1 after mention of our sod house with a sod roof, the house in which I was born. It is hoped these diversions may be a source of relief and pleasure also for the reader, and that they may not prove serious distractions. These bits about the birds, flowers and the Pacific are so intrinsic a part of my emotional and intellectual life that for this account to fully reveal the vital and consequential factors in the life of the writer it would seem these diversions must be written into this story. They add another dimension for this study.

My stuttering has long ceased to be an albatross around my neck, but the stuttering is still in me. Sometimes I *feel* the sensation or tension of a stutter in my mouth when I have made no sound or movement for speech. I lose no opportunity to speak of my stuttering, and the more I do mention my stuttering and use prolongations, even very short ones, in my talking the more dependable my speech is. It was so nearly normal during my last dozen or so years in Racine, and continues to be so during my retirement in San Diego that friends, associates and casual acquaintances do not, cannot think of me as a stutterer, but if I should attempt to pass as a normal speaker, the stuttering would be there—and soon would be quite obvious. But, also, may I say, I know of no one who has stuttered into adult years who has made a more stable, dependable and comfortable recovery than I have. From a tense, rather anxious, somewhat insecure young person, the events of my life have left me a calm, assured, relaxed, accepting person. It is far the best mental-hygiene attitude to continue to acknowledge my stuttering, and to think of myself as a stutterer, but *a stutterer who now can do anything*.

I have been more concerned with the treatment of stuttering than with the cause. There may be neurological factors that tend to produce stuttering, but I am certain there are emotional influences that tend to precipitate the stuttering. When circumstances are such that an individual identifies himself as a stutterer, it is probable that some

xviii

degree of stuttering may continue as long as that individual lives. The important thing is to change the stuttering pattern so it ceases to be a professional or a social handicap, and so that the individual may learn how to become a calm, relaxed person. My experience with my own stuttering and with trying to help other stutterers leads me to feel it is a myth that girls recover from stuttering more readily than boys—especially when the stuttering persists into the adult years.

I feel assured in stating that if I could have had such a book as this one during my high school years, my years at the university, or during my early teaching years I could have and would have helped myself to better speech.

Along with Dr. Van Riper, I feel the circumstances associated with my stuttering have enriched my life. The study and training in speech pathology, the treatment for my stuttering and my years in Racine, Wisconsin, gave me a richer, fuller life than I probably would have experienced otherwise.

Ida E. Whitten

5821 Gullstrand Street
San Diego, California 92122

"The Face of All the World is Changed."

An Autobiographical Study with the
Focus on Stuttering.

CHAPTER 1

MY PIONEER ANCESTRY

LIGHT AND COOLNESS from the open kitchen door and brightness from the south and east windows flooded our kitchen that fine summer morning. I see myself clearly, a small child of two or three years, but my dear mother only dimly in the shadow. I was intent on getting some fact or point of view across to her. I was tense and excited, full of stress, whether from what I was trying to tell her, or from her reaction to my effort, I know not. Maybe it was a joy to share with her, possibly something about the chickens in the yard, or the farm animals not far away. My mother was responding not to my idea, but to my way of speaking—to the way my sounds came out.

"Poor little girl."

In memory I hear my mother's voice. There is sadness, disappointment, almost despair, but also great love, gentleness, sweetness, pity and deep concern in the voice I hear. Possibly from her subconscious point of view, if I, her wanted child, could not speak well, I had failed her. On at least one occasion I asked my mother what she meant. Her answer is lost, blurred beyond recognition over the intervening years.

My parents said I stuttered when I learned to talk, that sometimes I stuttered very severely then. Evidently there was in my speech from the beginning that which my parents identified as stuttering. On the other hand, from an objective, professional point of view, it would seem, there was some repetition of sounds, some irregularity in the rhythm of my speech at times, during all my early years, and then my first year or so in school, but without my being much aware that my speech might be different from the speech of others. I do have the impression, the exceedingly faint memory, that on this occasion when my mother said "Poor little girl" I was excited and that I was dimly aware of irregularities in my speech. Perhaps I was an excitable child, overly excitable at times.

But beyond this, deeper still, there is an intensely persistent impression from my earliest years that there was something I did not understand—that I could not comprehend. Or, was there something, clear to me, that my mother did not understand about me—or about the situation? There was something, it would seem, my child mind could not fathom, something that left this questioning doubt in my memory from so many years ago.

Why do I remember this so clearly? Even then at age two, three, or so I may have had a slight awareness of a difference in my speech. Or, more important for a small child, I may have become aware of my parents' reaction to irregularities in my speech. I seem to have sensed the dreadful seriousness of something about me, and I may even then have sensed that the problem was in the repetitions in my speech.

4

But again I seem to feel I was not aware of a speech difference until later. I seem to have no memory of what we identify as stuttering until I was nine years or so old and in school. This is a significant point.

For this account to be of real value, my story must be as exact and accurate as it is humanly possible for me to write it. My memories, impressions from those early years are faint, faint as a distant echo, but persistent as the Kansas spring winds. I have the impression that on rare occasions I might be, or at least might seem to be, unreasonable. At such incidents it took time for my devoted, sensitive mother to calm me and bring me back to being the quiet, sweet child I ordinarily was. Perhaps at such times there were an undue number of irregularities, repetitions in my speech.

My mother had been a teacher before her marriage so she was aware of what such a speech deviation might mean later in every phase of family, educational, business, professional or married life for me. My mother's nephew, Norman Howe, had what seemed to me a mild stutter, but there were some irregularities in his speech all his life. He became a manual training teacher, so his speech was not so much a handicap as for more formal teaching. Norman was some twelve years older than I was, so my mother knew about stuttering.

"Poor little girl."

MANY MEMORIES, it would seem, were pushed back into the unconscious mind. (Here *unconscious* is used in the Freudian sense.) The events of my growing-up years shaped me into the individual who would have to deal with my stuttering when it became such I could no longer endure to live with it. Some have termed their stuttering a Monster. In truth, I must say I never felt that. It was some fault or event or condition within me that eventually had to be changed. The environment in which stuttering developed and persisted must be a matter of concern for an in-depth study of an individual with a stutter.

My brother's baby pictures show him quiet, calm, relaxed; my baby pictures show me a wide-eyed, alert, active infant. Pictures taken when I was perhaps a year and a half old show the same happy, alert, active, fussily-dressed little girl. Photos of my brother as a small child show him quiet, serious, relaxed and intent on his activity. This was a difference of temperament, for my brother was just as capable a young person and adult as I was. We were of decidedly different dispositions. I was four and a half years older than Harold. I remember him at his play always earnest, sober, unruffled, and concentrated on his momentary activity.

People seemed not to be aware of the young age at which small children pick up bits of adult conversation. The danger is that a child may distort the meaning of what he hears. I distinctly remember my mother saying one afternoon when we had company "We planned for Ida, but Harold just came along." Years later when Harold was in his forties, he once said to me "They wanted you."

I feel certain both my parents loved and cared most deeply for both Harold and me. It seems to me that at times my mother was trying to win Harold's love. Such a burden as Harold carried in his heart all those years! Maybe that is one reason he was such a serious, somber little boy.

THE FAMILIES of both my parents were of pioneer origin.

Grandfather Whitten owned a farm in eastern Nebraska. Grandmother Whitten was married when she was but thirteen or fourteen years old; she was not even certain of her birthdate. There was a step-mother, so marriage for her was an escape. My father's older brother told what a fine-looking couple Grandfather and Grandmother Whitten were when they were young. There were a good many Biblical names in that family of two parents and ten children. Not long before the turn of the century several members of the family moved to northwestern Kansas.

Grandfather Howe was a sawyer in southwestern Iowa. (A sawyer is "one whose occupation is to saw wood.") His first wife and several of their children died of tuberculosis. So Grandfather and Grandmother Howe, my maternal grandparents, were near forty or older when they married. My mother and her brother were never quite as hardy and rugged as many people. It seems significant that they were the offspring of older parents. When Grandmother Howe was widowed my mother was only two or three years old. Not long after that Grandmother brought her two small children, Uncle Will and my mother, to western Kansas in a covered wagon drawn by a team of horses. Grandmother's daughter by an earlier marriage lived in western Kansas. Grandmother Howe was a capable, practical person.

The big family Bible that was brought west in the covered wagon was handed down by way of the youngest daughter. It was leather bound, printed in England "by John Baskett, Printer to the University, MDCCXXXVIII," (1738). It is ten by eight inches in size, three inches thick. The family records are in most beautiful handwriting, but with flourishes that make it extremely difficult to make out some words and their exact spelling. My mother knew we were eligible for membership in Daughters of the Revolution, but she did not have the records. That Bible contains ten books of the Apocrypha, some of which are quite long. The print is good size, and the book is very readable save that the letter "s" is made almost like the "f", however one soon becomes accustomed to that, and can read right along. I recall reading some of those Apocryphal stories when I was eleven or twelve years old. They are not much like the scriptures. That Bible is falling to pieces now, but it is a precious heirloom. I have known since my earliest childhood that the "Old Bible" was to be mine.

My parents were thirty years old when they married at the turn of the century. They lived on their own eighty-acre farm a few miles south of Phillipsburg in northwestern Kansas. My father raised corn since the land was too hilly for wheat. He had a few horses, enough to farm with, a few cows and pigs. In those early years my father walked behind his horse-drawn implements—the plow, the lister, the cultivator. We were poor, but not so poor as some of our neighbors for we did own our farm.

My mother raised chickens and a few turkeys. Every week she churned cream to get butter. I clearly see her sitting sedately beside the churn moving the long wood dasher rhythmically up and down for twenty minutes or more. That buttermilk, left after the cream was churned, was a special treat. My mother sold eggs and butter at the store in Phillipsburg. It was that "egg and butter" money that paid for the necessities—flour, sugar, coffee, and occasionally some wearing apparel.

One store, Renick's, paid or allowed a cent or two

8

more for eggs, butter and poultry, but they paid in scrip or credit, not in United States money. My parents did not like the scrip for it was accepted only at Renick's store. The pieces of scrip that I remember resembled real coins, but they were thin and made of base metal. It may be from the effects of the October 1907 Panic that I have these memories. I have just been reading that sometimes panic conditions existed at the same time in European countries. At that time panics occurred fairly regularly every few years. During a financial panic there was an unusual scarcity of money. Then United States coins contained an amount of silver equal to the face value of the coin, but that has gradually changed. Many people, when they had a little extra money, would put it in a baking powder can with a tight lid and bury the can in the ground. People did not trust paper money. In 1933 President Roosevelt closed the banks for three days to save the economy at that time.

On the eighty acre farm where I was born there was a one-room sod house with a wooden floor and a sod roof. How I wish I knew more about that sod roof. (Mention of our sod house has always touched a sensitive nerve, so to ease that feeling my thoughts flit to early homes I saw in Norway and Sweden when I traveled there in 1963. In their "Outdoor Museum" there are speciments of early homes with turf roofs. Grass grew on the turf, even wild flowers grew and bloomed there. A lamb might be put on the roof for safety from the wolves.)

DURING THE two years my parents lived on the eighty-acre farm there was some degree of crop failure because of lack of rain. My parents could not but feel insecurity,

9

even anxiety regarding the matter of how they would supply the necessities of life. I recall my father telling that the winter before I was born in August, he herded cattle for a neighbor for fifty cents per day. I have a fine china plate my father got for my mother that Christmas.

"I wanted to get your mother something." I clearly recall my father saying that in the 1960s when he was in his nineties and living with me in Racine. During all our years in Kansas we used that fine china plate, made in Germany, as a bread plate. The metal handle that curved over the plate finally corroded and was discarded. There is a picture on the plate of the Phillipsburg school building, quite a fine wooden, two-story structure. Phillipsburg was a small, western, railway-division town. Many years later it had a population of 4000.

When I was seven months old my parents moved to a different farm. They sold the eighty-acre farm and bought the 160 acre place just east of Grandfather Whitten's farm. That was eight miles north of Phillipsburg. My earliest memories are from the years we were living in the fine new sod house Grandfather Whitten helped build for us. Grandfather's judgment in regard to building was sound for he had built frame houses. It is hardly child's play to construct even a sod house. Grandfather, Uncle Ephraim and my father put up our two-room house. It had a wooden floor and a shingled roof. The ceiling and roof were the same as for a frame house. Two-by-fours were fixed across the sod walls to form the ceiling. Then laths were nailed to those two-by-fours. After that the ceiling and the sod walls were plastered. The plaster, applied directly to the sod walls, made fairly smooth inside walls for our two rooms. Then the plaster of the walls and

10

ceiling was ready to be white-washed. Our two-room sod house was a fine, solid building. There were very few sod houses then, but I'm certain my parents felt it was all right for us to live in our new home for a few years.

There are some advantages for a sod house since it is cool in summer and warm in winter. The walls of a sod house are thick—eighteen inches or more. There were deep window seats. I distinctly recall being on the floor and using the window seat to write on. I have happy contented, peaceful memories and associations of our life in that quiet two-room sod house. Evenings our kerosene lamp gave a soft, warm light. The corn cobs burned quietly and slowly in the stove. That was long before radio and T.V. It was a happy home. We lived there for thirteen years.

Some of the positive points for our life on the prairies in northwestern Kansas in the early twentieth century are: The air was pure, sometimes dusty, but in the main it was good. Our water came from a deep well; hard water but good, pure and cold. The crops were grown on nearly virgin soil. No commercial fertilizers or sprays were used. We raised our own potatoes, and my mother always had some garden. Our livestock had the same advantages that we did.

DURING MY CHILDHOOD I recall various occasions on which my father jovially said, "I'm sure my family were very glad to have a boy after four girls." Being a boy after four girls certainly did give him more prestige in that family of ten children. My father always retained some of that feeling of his own intrinsic importance, along with pride in his personal appearance. He was trim and erect even into his nineties.

11

My mother was a sensitive, delicate, talented person, quite pretty when I was a child. She was small and slender—proud, too, with a natural refinement. The Kansas prairies were not kind to her. There was always the uncertainty of the crops and more or less anxiety over the future.

It seems natural that I have always been proud and wanted to appear at my best. That made the times in high school when I stuttered all the more devastating. I was rather a plain child, my hair was straight, not curly. There seems to have been some disappointment in this, that my hair was straight. My mother took such loving care of my hair when I was child that my braids were still neat at the end of the day. Mother and I wore sunbonnets to protect our faces and necks, for then it was not desirable to be tanned, but a small child cannot always be sunbonneted. Playing out on that Kansas hillside I must have been "Brown as a berry."

MY MOTHER was fond of her brother's children. After she was married she wanted a child; I think my father did, too. "I hoped and prayed you would live through that first day." I still clearly hear my mother's voice as she told me of my birth. "You had spasms." My mother used the plural form—spasms. I weighed eight pounds at birth. And then I cried. The neighbors told my parents I had the three-month colic, and that after that I would be all right, but I kept right on crying. I cried for nearly nine months. Both my brother and I were breast fed. Harold did not cry unduly, but he did have some food problems. My dear mother had a good deal of work to do: Housekeeping, baking bread, cooking, looking after the chickens, in addition to taking care of a crying baby. The laundry was done in a wash tub. Water was heated in a boiler on the stove, then the water was transferred to a wash tub. The clothing and bedding were rubbed by hand on a washboard. Some of the white pieces, such as dish towels, were boiled in the boiler to get them white. After the washing and rinsing the washed pieces had to be hung outdoors on a clothesline to dry. A prairie woman's life was not easy. My mother must have been worried and anxious about her infant who cried so much of the time. I feel certain I was never neglected. Some of the work had to be let go.

In later years I recall my mother telling a bit ruefully that when my father came in from the field he would hold me and I would stop crying. This may be significant. My father was tired from working in the field all day, but happy and relaxed to be home with his wife and baby. In other words, his "muscle tensions" were good. Even as a baby I must have sensed that relaxation, and could in turn relax—young infant as I was. That is my interpretation after many years of study and observation.

CHAPTER 2

EARLY MEMORIES

THEY KEPT ME in the kitchen, and if I said something or cried they just said "Sh---." Even my father did that. How I wanted and needed my gentle mother. Once when my father came out of the other room he was wiping his eyes. I said, "I want my mamma," and tears ran down my cheeks. Father tried to fix our big, high-backed, old-fashioned, wooden rocking chair so I could almost lie down in it. Then he told me I should go to sleep. His voice sounded strange. I so needed to hear my mother's soothing voice and to feel her caressing touch.

Perhaps events were something like that. Two years after I was born my mother gave birth prematurely to a still-born baby. After that she was critically ill for a time. It is a marvel she recovered. What a sad fate mine would have been had I not had my patient, forgiving mother all those years. I have a clear memory from the next day. There was an object I thought I could play with. A doll? It must have been the baby that didn't live.

Those days, while my precious mother was so ill, assuredly were a sad time for the little two-year old I was then, a time of tremendous uncertainty, my speech not yet firmly established. How I needed to feel my mother's loving touch and hear her comforting voice.

Aunt Mercy, my father's oldest sister, came several times to help us while my mother was so ill, but this is the one time I recall. My one memory of that day is that Aunt Mercy fixed a basin with a little water in it and let me carry it to my mother's bed so my mother could wash her hands before our noon meal.

"You see you are a real help." Those kind words from my aunt show she realized something of the uncertainty and anxiety I was experiencing while my mother was so ill. Aunt Mercy was not so beautiful as some of her sisters but none of the others were quite so gentle and understanding. Her name fitted her—she had the quality of mercy. Those assuring words and the distinctive quality of Aunt Mercy's kind voice of more than eighty years ago are as clearly fixed in my memory as though it were but yesterday that she said "You see you are a real help." My special affection for her surely came from that time. When we went to visit Aunt Mercy and Uncle Riley she served my parents hot tea and sometimes a doughnut with a bit of chocolate frosting. The geraniums in her windows smelled spicy.

This memory of the object I thought I could play with and the wash basin is quite an early one. I was two years, a little less or more. It seems possible, or even probable the stress of that time had a relation to my stuttering.

ANOTHER INCIDENT from those early years is that one spring day my mother took me, clinging tightly to her hand, to the pasture to pick daisies. That surely was an outing, a walk that was talked about, planned and antic-

16

ipated because I remember it so distinctly. This walk was important for my mother as well as for me. For my mother, with her need for beauty, the daisies were a herald of spring. No other blooms were as early or quite so symbolic. Daisies were small white spring flowers in pastures all over the mid-western states—now they may be rare. The blooms close at night and open again when the sunshine warms them a bit. They are without much fragrance, but lovely as only an early wild spring flower can be. Blue daisies were rare even then. Once my father brought home a few blue daisies he had found. There was no talk of conservation of wild flowers then. The daisies were really Carolina Anemone. William Chase Stevens writes of them: ''The flower is often mistaken for a daisy—no description or photograph can recapture the enchantment of these flowers for those who experienced it in pioneer days when in early April in delicate tints it overspread the prairie around homes and schoolhouses and away toward the horizon . . .'' (p. 65)

My mother and I walked on a southern slope with a light wind in our faces, looking for the daisies. The buffalo grass was well pastured as it had not yet grown much that early in the spring. The daisies were more likely to be found on a bank or inside a fence where our livestock did not graze. I'm certain we did find daisies, but I have no memory of that. It was a rather gray April day, cold but the snow was gone.

My next memory picture is that my mother, father and I were standing in our cozy kitchen. I was still bundled up. There was a note of questioning in my mother's voice as she told my father, ''Ida couldn't *see* the daisies. I had to show them to her.'' I still have the memory of hearing

17

my mother saying those words. The reason I couldn't see the daisies? I am near-sighted. I have a wonderful pair of eyes, but well along in my eighties I am still near-sighted. I was approximately two and a half or three and a half years old. Harold was not born.

When my father was working near the house, but not with horses, I liked to be out with him. I remember asking him questions, questions about what he was doing and why. I wanted to understand, but my questions must have bothered him when he was busy for I have a distinct memory he would soon send me in the house. He would say "I think your mother wants you in the house." I would mind reluctantly, and it must have been with some hurt, for I do recall vividly that I wanted to be out with my father and I did want explanations of what he was doing and why.

There were a few scrawny peach trees between our sod house and the road, seedlings, certainly not grafted trees. One of my earliest memories is of being up in one of those small, scrub peach trees, up one high step, high for a three or four year old. I could almost see into the nest but the birds were making a fuss. The sky was a pallid gray from dust in the air. The wind was blowing, not a gale, but still a fairly strong Kansas spring wind. My curiosity and perhaps my loneliness led me to climb that small tree.

An hour later my mother found mites in my hair. I was impatient while my mother tried to comb out those mites. She kept parting my hair and combing. "We have to get the mites out, Darling, or they will lay nits on your scalp." Mother's voice was soothing and calming. I knew about mites and their nits on my mother's chickens.

18

"That sparrow's nest!" I hear my father's voice. Mother had wondered how I got mites in my hair. She washed my hair with egg shampoo—a raw egg beaten and used as shampoo. I have never liked the smell of egg.

I climbed that little tree to investigate a sparrow's nest. I have always been curious about everything. The images in my memory from that time are faint, faint as a fading dream, yet indelible as though etched in steel. What a difference between those poor, stunted peach trees with those sparrows and their mites as contrasted with the splendid, grafted apple and peach trees we had after we moved to the Grandpa farm.

My memories from those early years are like photographs—not moving pictures. A point which seems strange to me is that I see myself in these memory pictures.

I have few recollections from those early years. Some threatening ones may have been pushed back into the unconscious and seemingly forgotten. The memories I do have would seem to be significant. Aunt Mercy praised me. That must have been a comfort. After the daisy-picking incident something was observed to be amiss. I could not *see* the daisies. There was a threat about the mites. If we did not get them out of my hair they would lay nits on my scalp.

But what of all the joyous, tender, loving moments and events? I am certain there were many instances every day that should give assurance to me a little child. My parents by word and deed made my days happy, contented and even joyous, but there is only a general assurance of these feelings in my memory.

OF ALL the Kansas blizzards I recall but one. Some

blizzards last three days. The gusty, biting wind swirls the snow into huge drifts, some fantastically shaped. Other areas are swept bare. A farmer could be lost on his own land. After the livestock are cared for there is only one thing for farm people to do—stay in the house. Once my father drew a checkerboard with heavy lead-pencil marks on a piece of cardboard. Then my parents used black and white buttons for checkers.

One such day I teased to go outside. It was dull to be inside all day, even with my father in the house. Inside our snug, warm sod house one could never guess the howling winds were raging and tearing outside. The snow piled up around the windows thus adding insulation. Finally toward evening my father did wrap me up well and let me go out the south door where there was not much snow and the wind did not get a full sweep. I knew it was great fun to walk on top of frozen, queer-shaped drifts, but that snow near the south door was still soft so I sank down in it. I remember walking slowly to the corner of the house, possibly twenty feet. There the full fury of the penetrating icy north wind caught me.

"Oh, the wind took my breath."

How my father laughed as he let me in and took off my wet overshoes.

My parents must have told that story a few times and laughed. Now with the wisdom of the years in my mind and after much psychological study, I reflect how simple it would have been for one of my parents to take me by the hand, warn me about the stinging wind and the cutting, piercing snow. Then we together after a very few moments outside, could decide it was too windy for a walk that day. I do not blame my parents in the least. They gave my brother and me love overflowing, but I have had the advantage of psychological and psychoanalytical study. (It is painful for me to write of this even now, so many years later. I find relief as I become aware of the festive fragrance of the three fine gardenia blooms I just brought in from my big bush. The largest of these blooms is four and a fourth inches in diameter, large for a gardenia. The waxy-white petals stand out from each other, so these freshly-cut blooms have depth as well as width.) Adults should not talk about children in their presence even when those children are quite small—less than a year old.

THEN IT WAS the first of April. "Ida! Get up, Ida! We have puppies." I still hear the note of urgency in my father's voice that April Fool's Day morning. My brother and I knew our dog was going to have puppies, and we would keep one for our farm dog. We were so eager to have the puppies come that every day we asked how soon they would be born. That morning our father had the dog shut up in a box some twenty feet from the south kitchen window. Part of an old comforter, thrown over the box and held in place by a large clay-colored rock, was flapping erratically in the wind. Ordinary window glass at that time had defects that distorted parts of what one saw, so if one moved ever so slightly the box and piece of flapping comforter changed shape and dimensions.

"It's April Fools' Day, Sweetheart." Mother spoke softly. She didn't want me to be deeply disappointed. So I knew it was a trick, but still I was curious. I had to go out to look, in part because my father wanted me to. I would do anything in the wide world to please him! Then how my father did laugh! I was not much hurt, but on the other hand I do remember this incident most clearly. How that comforter flapped! Harold was too young to be April fooled.

I had grown up feeling it was quite the thing to fool someone on April Fools' Day, but when I April-fooled the school superintendent at Imperial, Nebraska, he didn't think it was funny. Early the morning of April first I called him to come see what confusion someone had made in my classroom. After I said "April fool" I realized he didn't like my joke!

In due time the puppies were born. How Harold and I did play with them. We kept one black puppy. Mother named him Diogenes. (According to the encyclopedia Diogenes was an ancient Greek philosopher whose nickname was Dog.) We all called him Die, he was such a dear puppy. He was all Harold and I had to pet. I did not mind if he licked my hand, or even my chin with his little rough, red tongue. Every day I carried Die around.

Die became an excellent farm dog. We all loved him, but he was a work dog, not just a pet. He knew exactly how to keep the cows moving. If one lagged behind, he would nip that cow's heels. Anyone coming to our door needed to beware or Diogenes would nip his heel. We were his family and he was taking care of us.

HAROLD WAS FOUR and a half years younger than I was. I fear I was not a very loving and considerate big sister for this baby brother. I was a petted, humored child, so I suspect I greatly resented my rival, this baby brother. As I recall while we were growing up we played together very little, but once we were having a fine time together making mud-pies and laying them out to dry. I went in

22

the house to ask for something we needed in making the pies.

"What are you going to do with them?" my mother asked.

That was certainly the wrong question! The fun was in the making of the pies, not what we would do with them.

Harold was quite a serious little boy. Mother read that a boy should have a hammer, nails and boards, I suppose to work off his aggression. So mother got Harold a small hammer, then every now and then she would buy him quite a sack of smallish nails. He drove his nails into wood from orange crates.

Father had named me for his favorite sister. Mother named Harold. She gave him a name she liked. Mother always called us Harold and Ida, save for occasional endearing terms. Father called me Ide—as long as I can recall it was Ide. When Harold was quite small, father called him Heddo. Father, it seems to me, felt a special deference for his small son, a recognition of Harold's potential. There was a special quality and consideration in our father's voice whenever he addressed Harold, even when Harold was quite small. When my brother was a few years older and could help some around the farm father began calling him Whit. There was a very strong bond between father and son. From the time I can recall father addressed Harold as an individual of worth and importance.

ONE RECOLLECTION I would prefer to forget is that I would sometimes pout and not talk when things did not go to suit me. Only one incident I recall. I was tired of

23

pouting and wanted to be friends again, but how to change from pouting to being friends again! It is amazing to me how clearly my feelings of that moment, eighty years ago, come back to me. For a short time I was a miserable little girl! My mother chided me by saying I did not look pretty with my lips stuck out. Father said my lips stuck out like a bridge one could walk across.

ANOTHER CRYSTAL-CLEAR MEMORY—my mother was standing at one end of the kitchen table kneading the bread dough. Dough should be kneaded twenty to thirty minutes. This kneading can be a loving process, a way of caressing the dough. Of course my mother baked our bread. At that time every Kansas farm woman baked bread for her family. Sometimes my mother let us eat the "heel" of the loaf while it was still warm. Such good bread!

"Do you love me, Mother?" I was sitting at the other end of the table.

I see my mother standing there kneading the bread. It was cool weather for the kitchen door was shut. Mother was wearing a long dress with long sleeves and a collar, as women did then, in darker dull colors, not bright colors as we wear now. Mother's long dark hair was done up on her head. I feel certain I had no reason to doubt my mother's deep affection for me. I had not been punished, indeed I was rarely punished. A word of correction was punishment for me, I was so sensitive.

"Of course I love you, Darling." Mother's voice was soft and gentle, reassuring of her constancy.

Father sometimes laughed heartily and told stories of "back in Nebraska." Then my mother would laugh too, but she never seemed to tell stories—life was a serious

24

matter. With ten children in the Whitten family, life must have been lively during my father's growing-up years. I remember my father's brothers and sisters, my aunts and uncles, as always being lively and full of the joy of living. On the other hand in my mother's early years there may have been many quiet, lonely times. Possibly she was a lonely little girl, as I now feel that I was. Perhaps my real question to my mother was if you really love me why isn't life more lively, more interesting, more fun?

In my early childhood I had only one or two books. Phillipsburg had no library until years later. When I was seven years old my mother got me a First Grade Reader. There was a doll, Hildegarde, but I seem not to have played much with her. She had a china head with the hair painted black and lying in waves. Her cheeks were pink and she had a pretty smile. Remember that was soon after the turn of the century. I do seem to have had some affectionate regard for the doll. I recall several different times the head got broken. Then my mother would buy a new head and sew it on to the body. A cat would have been more interesting for me than any inanimate doll.

CHAPTER 3

LIGHTNING STRIKES OUR HOUSE

(This morning the Pacific is a somber steel blue. There is none of the sparkle as though ten thousand diamonds were floating on the surface of the water, the facets of each diamond reflecting the sun's rays. The breakers are rolling in slowly, each of the large ones like a Niagara advancing steadily toward the shore. On Sundays after church I drive the short distance down to the ocean. Even with the sky leaden-gray the air off the Pacific is exhilarating. I stand looking, dreaming, reminiscing for a time.)

OUR HOME was more than half a mile from any neighbor, for western Kansas was sparsely settled. When I was three or four years old a rural telephone line was put in, so then we had a telephone; but that was something of a luxury for it cost a dollar per month. I vividly remember my father's telephone call to his brother's family the morning after Harold was born. I was surprised at my father's words and didn't quite understand what he meant. "We have a wood chopper." My cousin also recalls those exact words spoken by my father more than eighty years ago.

Some of the electrical storms were terrifying for me, frightening for all of us. One might notice after such a storm that another telephone pole along the road had been struck by lightning. One evening during a storm, there came a crash of thunder as though a thousand bass drums were struck at the same instant, and simultaneously a flash of lightning such that for a moment our house was better lighted than on a bright sunshiny day. My parents saw a ball of fire the size of a man's fist come down by the north window of the bedroom. The lace curtain at that window was on fire, and the corner of the bed nearest that window was beginning to burn. Harold, less than a year old, was asleep on that bed. Mother snatched up Harold. He was unharmed and still asleep. Father put out the flames. I was in a panic! The rain was coming down in torrents. The featherbed under Harold probably served as a protection for him. We had to have a different curtain for that window, but we used the bedspread for years, even with a three-inch hole in one corner.

ONE OF MY FATHER'S ROUTINE tasks was to carry two big pails of water every morning from the windmill to the house—a distance of perhaps two blocks with part of the way uphill. We were as saving of water as we were of money. Evenings we lighted a kerosene lamp. I have one in San Diego from our Kansas home which I sometimes light to eat by in winter. It gives a little warmth in addition to light and a special kind of cheer.

28

At times there were arguments between my parents. Strong words were sometimes spoken, but on the whole I think my parents were happy together and proud of each other. Yet at some times in my childhood I did worry about how bad it would be if my parents should separate. I wanted both of them together in our home. On the whole it seems to me now I felt quite secure during my childhood. I vaguely recall many happy, peaceful times. Memories of our evenings carry especially precious associations. The heating stove was also the cookstove. Cold evenings as we sat close around the stove we would often have the oven door open to help heat the room.

My mother had a good deal of adaptability. She liked twilight time. My memory is that she made those times radiantly warm with her affection for us, for the well-being of all her attention encompassed. Once my mother sent for a book of Bible stories, a thick blue book. On winter evenings my mother and father took turns reading those stories aloud. I have a warm, cozy feeling when I think back to that time. Those evenings may be my happiest, most secure, childhood memory.

These memories are most precious treasures, enough to bring peace when circumstances may be troubling. The warmth of my parents' love for each other and their love and concern for my brother and me brightened our evenings together and made them a living treasure in my memory. Those evenings are not picture-memories, but rather a synthesis—a sum total of the warmth, the love, the joy, the closeness, the oneness of our family. What a happy, content, confident little child I was those evenings. Possibly those times were laying the foundations for strengths, resources I would have vast need for later.

It seems to me my parents were always able to meet emergencies and make the best of whatever the conditions were.

Corn cobs were our chief fuel. They are convenient to burn and essentially clean. For the very coldest weather father sometimes bought some coal, but coal was expensive, and dirty to burn. We preferred the corn cobs.

Sunday mornings we went to Sunday School in the one-room school building. Sometimes there was a Methodist minister on alternate Sundays.

KANSAS IS almost as well-known for its tornadoes as California is known for its earthquakes. We called them cyclones or twisters. Two different years, while we lived in the sod house, a tornado came down five or six miles southwest of our home and did damage. After one tornado my father took us to see the path the storm had taken. There was a swath through a golden-yellow field of wheat that looked as though it had been mowed. Once my father went to offer help. A woman and her little girl were killed in that storm. I don't remember my father saying much about what he saw, but after that when a storm came we all went to the cellar, Diogenes with us.

Just before the full force of a savage storm struck, while the black clouds were churning and racing, sometimes in different directions, there might be a great, heavy encompassing silence, that lasted but a few moments just before the storm began to vent its fury. That was a silence, a stillness such as one remembers a lifetime. When there is a tornado, whether or not the funnel-shaped cloud touches the ground, often a small number of extraordinarily large hailstones fall in some small area. Once a few huge hailstones, possibly two dozen, fell near our windmill. From our house we heard them hitting the ground. After the storm my father carried four of them to the house, four was all he could carry on one hand for they were larger than golf balls.

Some people had a concrete cave built into a bank, but ours was just a dirt cellar with a roof of tarred timber covered with dirt. One had to have a cool place to keep eggs, milk and butter. Ours served the purpose very well, and also provided a safe shelter during a severe storm.

One spring, perhaps before I started to school at the age of nine years, I heard two neighbor women seemingly speaking seriously and saying that the long coarse hairs from a horse's mane or tail, when left in water, could turn into worms. Many people at that early time still clung to a few superstitions, "old wives" sayings. When I asked my mother if that were true about the horsehairs her reply was "Watch and see what happens," so I watched. It was a rainy time, and down by the windmill water stood in puddles, even in horses' hoofprints. Every day or sometimes more often I would go down by the windmill to look at those horsehairs in the puddles of water. It made something for a lonely little girl to do. As some of the puddles began to dry out I poured more water in to be certain there was plenty of water for those horsehairs. I had the impression my mother was not certain about the horsehairs, thus I did my observations in part to find out so I might share my findings with her. I don't recall exactly what she said when I told her the horsehairs stayed just horsehairs, but she did not let me feel my observations were unimportant. That was my first scientific experiment.

This may seem a simple incident, but on analysis it is

31

significant and prognostic for my future. Why did I do this? I wanted to know. Even at that time I could define the problem and act independently. I understood the conditions needed to test the question: Could horsehairs turn into worms? I was consistent in my daily observations and care. No one knew I was watching the horsehairs so no one could remind me. I followed through for several weeks, possibly as long as six, or even eight weeks, to obtain a definitive answer to my question. Most important of all I was persistent! Now as I write this, I wonder why no one knew I was watching the horsehairs.

There is one other memory, so fleeting it seems trivial, but this one memory fairly shouts, as it were, to be noticed. One winter evening we were sitting close to the stove for warmth. A child likes to be held for it is warmer, softer and in general cosier to be held than to sit on a wooden chair. I was on my father's lap. I recall his words and his matter-of-fact tone of voice as he said, "You sit over there, you're heavy." And father put me over on a chair beside his. From the ease with which he lifted me, I may have been between two and three years old. To my child mind this was a kind of rejection. I have no memory of sitting on my mother's lap. Perhaps she had explained to me I was getting heavy and weighed too much for her to hold me. If my father had explained to me that I weighed as much as a large sack of sugar or a big bag of potatoes I would have understood. It seems I felt a great need to please my father. You recall on April Fool's Day I went out to see the puppies because he wanted me to.

NOW A STORY about my mother and her hen: "Come in Biddy." My mother spoke softly as she opened the

32

screen door. Biddy made gentle responses as she always did. She came in, walked sedately, almost majestically, to the place she was accustomed to sit and then lay her egg. She flew up there, slowly turned around a time or two, making her gentle hen-sounds as she did so. In memory I see and hear her clearly. I could pet her then for a moment—stroke her feathers quietly, but then my mother did not want me to disturb Biddy while she was sitting, getting ready to lay her egg. My mother had a hollowed-out place for the hen to sit and then lay her egg, hollowed-out so an egg could not roll off. Biddy would sit quietly for twenty minutes or so before she laid her egg. Shortly after that Biddy would fly down and move quietly, and with solemn dignity, toward the door to go outside. Sometimes she made her friendly, gentle hen sounds. It was the same hen that came in every day.

I don't know how it came about, but for a number of years a hen would come in the house to lay her egg. Hens may become quite tame, especially after they have raised a brood of chicks. We talked to the chickens much as we did the dog and cat. Potato peelings and other food scraps were thrown out in the yard and the chickens would eat them, so there were often a few chickens near the kitchen door. If we were gone all day my mother would worry a little about the hen. Sometimes on returning home we would find an egg by the doorstep.

My mother must have been lonely, so the hen was just a different kind of pet. This began during our early years in the sod house, and from summer to summer there must have been a number of different hens. After we moved to the Grandpa house my mother still had a pet hen that came in the house to lay her egg. This must have gone on over a twenty year period, or even longer. I never knew of any other person who let a hen in the house to lay her egg.

The reader may think this was strange. I feel it shows my mother's humanity—her consideration for animals as well as for people. This was one way of meeting loneliness, another example of problem solving. If my mother was a bit lonely, she was less lonely when a friendly hen wanted to come in. My mother treated people and animals—even hens—so as to bring out the best in them. Even a hen can behave responsibly when she is treated as a responsible creature.

My mother was a slight, dainty, idealistic person. She had a great gentleness, sweetness and consideration for others. She appreciated the beauty of the prairies, but the times of harshness and anxiety of our life were not suited for her gentle nature. She had a great love of the beautiful. She always had a few flowers in her garden. My mother was an excellent housekeeper and cook. She wanted her cakes to look beautiful as well as to taste fine, also she was aware of beautiful sounds as well as of beautiful sights. On winter evenings my mother often did some kind of handwork—embroidery, crocheting or tatting. She also found time to read the limited reading material that came into our home.

HOW THRILLED I was. A new book! A book with pictures of dogs, cats, birds, flowers and people. And stories about the pictures! I was going to learn to read! I was seven years old. My very own book! That September when the rural school began, my mother began teaching me at home. She would take me on her lap for an hour every

34

morning and teach me to read. I still have that little frayed book, Silver-Burdett Readers, printed in 1906. It is with deep emotion that I turn these pages. Our one-room country school was one and a half miles from our home. Kansas law was that a child must enter school by the age of eight, unless it was shown he was being taught elsewhere. My mother consulted with the teacher of our school from time to time to be certain I was doing work comparable to those attending school. I think my parents enjoyed having my brother and me at home. I felt it was splendid for my mother to teach me, and now I feel assured I was fortunate indeed to have a mother who could teach me at home. When I was nine years old I began attending the rural school. Then I was in the third grade. On some especially cold, snowy, stormy afternoons my father would walk to the school to bring me home safely. I was a loved and protected child.

Today at the library I came upon *The Tale of Peter Rabbit* by Beatrix Potter, reprinted by Knopf in 1982. There are 141 pages of delightful stories, enough to charm any child for a long time. There is at least one fine picture in color on each page. How different my life could have been when I was three, four and five years old could I have had a few such books.

"I don't believe you know all the words in your reader." I had asked my mother for something to do. I hazily hear her voice saying those words. So I read my reader over again to be certain I did know all the words. That time I read the book aloud. I remember feeling it was rather dull reading the same book over so many times. I had almost memorized some of the pages.

It seems strange that on a farm there were not enough

things to interest a little girl. I was safest, though, in the house with my mother. I think it would have been better had I been encouraged to be the Tom-boy type, to be a very active child. My mother tried to bring me up to be a lady. Once I dared to question her over something that some of the other children could do but that I was not allowed to do.

"You are one of the Blue Hen's chickens."

I understood what my mother meant. We were different from some of the neighbors. Perhaps the phrase Blue Hen related to the saying Blue Blood. The Blue Hen certainly had nothing to do with the chickens we raised.

IT WOULD have been better for me during my growing-up years to be more assertive. I was very dependent on those around me for approval. That is somewhat true for me even now. Some of my cousins were far more assertive than I was or have ever learned to be. I felt insecure unless I had the approval of my parents, my teachers, my associates. The blizzard incident in chapter two was one time I asserted my wishes—to go outside. Perhaps the pouting incident in the same chapter was also a time I tried to be assertive. A child needs explanations and reasons. While my mother was kneading the bread I asked if she loved me. If she did love me life should be more interesting, more challenging. Dreariness, I firmly believe, is one of the worst possible conditions. It could leave one without incentives to achieve better. I mention these points in part as suggestions of what parents may do to help a shy, unassertive child to a more healthy, secure adjustment.

CHAPTER 4

RURAL SCHOOL YEARS

THE COUNTY Superintendent of Schools visited each rural school every year. "What is that word?" That tall dignified man put his finger under a word in my reader.

When I had my turn at reading I must have miscalled one word. When I said the word over I had trouble getting the word out. I stuttered. That is what stuttering is—having difficulty getting a word said. Possibly even then in the third or fourth grade I had learned to substitute a word I could say for a word I would stutter on. I have a very negative memory of that county superintendent. Proud little child that I was, he had humbled me.

This seems to be my first memory of being identified as a stutterer. Not that the word stutterer was used, but at that moment I became aware my speech was at fault. I no doubt had heard the word stutter before that.

There is a persistent memory that my father had something do to with my substituting words. Father was an unusually practical man. On some occasions substituting words, using a word a stutterer can say in place of a word he would stutter on, may help a stutterer over a bad spot. Of course in the long run it is no help, for the stutterer may soon find himself stuttering on the substituted word.

MY PARENTS were most conscientious about being certain I learned what I should in school. Many evenings I said the multiplication tables through—as far as I had learned them. While my mother was clearing up after our supper and doing the dishes, my father listened to me saying the tables. We sat close to the stove, in winter we always sat close to the stove to keep comfortable. We did not burn any more corn cobs than was necessary. "3 times 6 is 18, 3 times 7 is 21...6 times 7 is 42." This was a kind of game, a challenge to get them all correct. It was something I did willingly. Along with all those tables I was learning persistence, to stay with a task until it is completed. As a child and young person I have little memory of helping much with the housework. The one thing that was expected of me was that I do well in school.

I have a persistent memory of at least on one occasion trying to get a number said without stuttering a little when I was saying those tables over in the evening. I wanted to conceal my stuttering. That early in my life there was anticipation of stuttering! Why did I want to conceal my stuttering? Had my family shown that repetitions were not acceptable? Some memories from those early years are extremely fragmented.

In fourth grade we had a geography book that was quite difficult, so my mother wanted me to bring that geography book home every afternoon so she could go over the lesson with me. Father helped me some with arithmetic. I well remember how nice it was having him help me with my problems. I schemed to get him to do some of the problems for me that I could do for myself, but before long he saw through that, so then I did my own problems.

That Christmas Santa brought me a Dissected Map of the United States. It was a bit like our jig-saw puzzles but in general each state was a separate piece. The map was perhaps twelve by eighteen inches in size. Such a pretty map it was when it was put together, each state was a different color or shade. For weeks every evening after supper I put that map together. At first my parents helped some, they enjoyed the puzzle, too. Thus I learned the states, their location and the capital of each state. It seems that was the only game or puzzle I had during my childhood. Later my mother bought a box of dominoes, then sometimes we all played dominoes together.

From those years I seem to have no other definite memory of stuttering, which only means there were no incidents of stuttering that were very threatening. Of course it is possible some memories of stuttering were pushed back into the unconscious.

THEN IT WAS spring, and springtime everywhere is a time of excitement and anticipation. It was time for our two rooms to be whitewashed as they were every spring. Father bought some lime, then one evening my parents ''slaked'' the lime. On this particular occasion it was after our supper, early dusk. A little water was thrown on the lime. I watched with fascination at a safe distance. Father stood far back and quickly stirred the lime with quite a long stick or pole. Great clouds of steam rose instantly when even a little water was added to the lime. When the lime was properly slaked the product was a white liquid which my parents used to whitewash the walls and ceiling of our sod house. This is an example of the know-how pioneers needed to carry on.

Every spring my father helped my mother with the housecleaning. There were two days of it, one for each room. A bright, clear day was essential, for all the furniture was moved out of one room, some of it carried outdoors. This was done early in the morning because the walls and ceiling had to dry after they were whitewashed. It should be a warm-enough day that the door could be left open for the whitewash to dry after it was applied. Then toward evening the furniture was moved back in. How wonderfully fine the house smelled after it was freshly whitewashed!

I knew my mother had a big can of salmon for the noon meal. Salmon was quite special for us at that time. My mother said she would save some salmon for me, for I would be at school at noon, but housecleaning day was a very special and exciting time! The work of the day was well underway before it was time for me to leave home for the mile and a half walk to school. My brother was not yet old enough to go to school.

"I don't feel very well," I said two or three times. Possibly the excitement did make my stomach hurt a little.

Finally my mother said, "If you don't feel well, you had better stay home." My mother was very busy that day. Then I was having a fine time playing, and helping now and then. I could carry outside small items such as bed slats.

"I don't believe you were sick at all," my mother finally observed, but by that time it was too late to go to school. It was not that I wanted to miss school but it was so exciting to be home that day, and then there was the salmon.

EVERY SUMMER there was more or less lack of rain. I recall the uncertainty and anxiety in my mother's voice: "Oh, if only it would rain! Every day there are more yellow tassels showing in the corn." The yellow tassels meant those stalks of corn were being hurt by lack of rain.

My father, it seemed to me, faced the problems as they came and tried his utmost to meet the situation and work things out as well as possible. I heard him say very little about problems. To me as a child and as a young person my father was the one who could do anything and everything. He did his very best to provide for us. If we had company he tried to make a joke about the drought. This shows an individual difference in the way my parents met a problem, but it also reveals the roles of a prairie wife and husband in the early twentieth century. The man made the basic decisions at that time.

If we did not raise enough corn to feed the chickens, the hens could not lay eggs for us to sell. In later years when my father had more cattle, it meant some of the cattle would have to be sold for there would not be feed for them.

On warm summer evenings we used to carry chairs outside and sit on the north side of our house during the early evening and then on into twilight time. There were seldom mosquitoes. Father's field of corn was in the distance, not far away on the west was grandfather's corn.

In present-day times when our streets, homes, yards

41

are so marvelously well lighted, it is difficult to experience the exquisiteness of dusk, and of dusk deepening into darkness. There is much fair weather in western Kansas. Frequently in the afternoon there are large, light, fleecy clouds floating lazily in the sky, but often the night sky is cloudless, so the heavens are a jewel-studded covering from horizon to horizon. The eyes adjust so one makes out a good deal even on a very dark night. We would look for star groups we knew, the Big and Little Dippers, and try to make out other star clusters. That night sky there over the prairies was very distant, so far above us. I remember the Kansas sky as usually being friendly and benevolent, as well as richly beautiful.

The elevation of Phillipsburg and the area of our farm is 2000 feet, so the nights were usually cool. As dusk came on it was delightfully pleasant outside in summer—the wind died down. Often there was sheet lightning in the distance. My mother knew that was an indication of drought. Sometimes as dusk deepened we saw fireflies. They are also an indication of drought.

Reminiscence of the delightful part of our evenings also brings remembrance of stress and anxiety, so my memories begin to wander, this time to the tour of Latin America I had in 1960. (The sky above Cuzco, Peru, was the bluest I ever saw, and so high, high above us. The elevation there is 11,297 feet, more than two miles. Then I remember Mt. Cotopaxi in Ecuador. Such a magnificent, yet tranquil view we had for an hour as our train moved along that peaceful, flower-covered slope. The 19,334 feet snow-capped extinct volcano is very near the Equator. The grandeur of such scenes as these has an enduring influence on the lives of those fortunate enough to view them. So it is with the Kansas sky—by day and at night, it is a delight and a beauty in my memory. I seem to forget the storms and remember that tranquil beauty.)

Then there is the magnificent silence of the prairies. Our livestock were far enough away so that we did not hear them, anyway they were sleeping. The chickens had long since gone to their roosts. The vegetation near was so scant there were not even bug sounds, just the great engulfing peace and quiet that lay like a blessing over those prairies. These are warm, sweet, happy, peaceful memories of our summer evenings sitting out on the north side of our home. It is my remembrance that a special mood of courage, of struggling through to some degree of success, settled over the land and enveloped us in the spirit of the pioneer. There must be a way.

(Again my memory wanders, this time to Athens, Greece. When I was there in 1963 the Acropolis was open to the public on three full-moon evenings. Our tour group attended a play in an ancient theatre at the foot of the Acropolis, then after the play we climbed up to the Acropolis. A very few of our group had flashlights, there were no electric lights. I was careful to hold someone's hand for the stones were slippery. Being on the Acropolis in full moonlight, with the peace and quiet of night, added to our comprehension of the vision of Greek thought and achievement of 500 B.C. It was another way of trying to understand the world of so long ago.)

Another aspect of the prairie was the buffalo wallow. The buffalo had been gone for fifty years or so, but some wallows remained. There was one in the pasture of our 160 acre farm. On the way to Phillipsburg we passed two large buffalo wallows. Buffalo like to roll or wallow in the dust, as birds and chickens like to flutter their wings in dust. Then water might collect where the buffalo had wallowed. The buffalo would drink the water and wallow in the mud and water. Eventually a wallow might get quite large—twenty or thirty feet across. In a rainy season they were like small ponds, but most of the year they were dry. My parents would sometimes comment about the water in the buffalo wallows when we were on the way to or from Phillipsburg.

IN AN EARLY DAY good homes had a reed organ. This instrument was in no way related to the present-day electric organ. Homes of more wealth had a piano. It was a social grace for one to be able to play an organ or a piano. Before her marriage my mother had a reed organ, but she gave it to her brother so his daughter could have music lessons. When I was nine or ten Uncle Will got a piano for his daughter, and gave the organ back to my mother. We made room for it in the two-room sod house.

Then I had music lessons for a few summers. I didn't practice very faithfully and there didn't seem to be much music in my fingers, but I did learn a good deal about music. That is, where the notes on a page of music are on the organ keyboard. Then there were sharps and flats to memorize. I wanted an explanation for the entire plan of sharps and flats, but my mother was afraid of confusing me if she gave me the entire explanation. I would ask her a few specific questions, thus finally I figured out the matter of sharps and flats for myself. I relate this to show the way my mind worked, and my persistence in finding out things. In part it was my curiosity, as with the matter of the horse hairs in the puddles of water.

44

With the organ in our home, I developed a great love of music, a deep gratification in beautiful sounds. While I was in college I managed to have some voice lessons. Thus I learned about abdominal breathing and the controlled use of the diaphragm to support a tone. I sang in the Messiah Chorus. Later in life I developed a deep appreciation and enjoyment of music, of whatever made beautiful sounds, be it clocks or bird songs. Much later at the Opera, my enjoyment of the lovely sounds was so great I cared very little about the story of the Opera.

By the time I was in the sixth or seventh grade at school we had a woman county superintendent of school, a Miss Thomas. I remember her as a splendid person, dignified but still approachable. There was a small traveling library in her office, really little more than a large box of books. I had a few of those books while we lived in the sod house. Miss Thomas would help me select a book. There were the Elsie Dinsmore books, and for the ones a little older, the Horatio Alger books. Later Harold Bell Wright's *Honorable Patches* was available.

Down a little hill west of our house there was a low area with a few small cottonwood trees and one quite large cottonwood. I had read a story of someone who read while perched up in a tree, so one day I climbed that big cottonwood with a book. I sat in a very uncomfortable position up in that big tree and read until I could endure the discomfort no longer.

It was in my early teens that I learned to lose myself in a book. It may seem I was naturally a student, but, rather I believe, books were a salvation for me since I had no playmates. It seems Harold and I did not play together much. I was to stay close to the house for safety. Some

45

children invent games to amuse themselves. It seems I did not do that. In school I did my best to please my parents and the teacher. There was an immense satisfaction in doing a thing well. Outside of school I turned to books for there was little else to involve my interest, so in a way books were my salvation. They relieved part of the boredom, they were in part a bridge to a most marvelous world of dreams and imaginings, so I was far less lonely than I otherwise might have been. Novels enriched my daydreams with characters and action.

Of course, being a farm child, I rode horseback. At first when I was quite a small child my father would lift me up on a horse that was wearing harness and I would hold on to the harness so I could not fall off. Later I think I rode horseback a few times holding on to the horse's mane. While we were still in the sod house my father got Fanny, and not long after that a saddle. Fanny was a treasure. She was gentle and dependable, a beautiful roan, quite delicately built. I don't think my father ever worked her in the field. A work horse holds its head about in line with its body, while a well-bred horse holds its head fairly high. Fanny's head was fairly high. Harold rode her for fun and for all sorts of errands. When my father left the farm he sold Fanny to a neighbor for a small price. He thought that neighbor would be good to Fanny for he wanted her to be well cared for.

WE WERE awakened early one spring morning, at two or three o'clock, in 1910, by light coming in the east and north windows. It was far too early for the sun and it was a different quality of light. My parents were alarmed that something might be on fire, but instead to the east and

46

a little to the north there was a great belt of light from the sky. That wide band of light came all the way down to the earth. No wonder I recall it so distinctly! Both my parents were practical. They did not speculate regarding possible supernatural causes, but they remembered reading that Halley's Comet was to appear. Little did we then comprehend the wonder of that early morning light, but now I realize we experienced a most remarkable and dramatic phenomenon, for that was the exact time in 1910 when the earth was passing through a part of the outer edge of the tail of Halley's Comet. That was the hour seventy-six years ago when the enormously long tail of Halley's Comet brushed the earth. (Seventy-six years until the Comet appeared again in 1986.)

The following explanation is from a "New York Times" article dated May 18, 1985: "The comet is a traveling mixture of rock and ice about four miles long. Think of it as a giant flying mountain full of primordial debris left over from the creation of the solar system. As that mountain nears the sun it starts to sweat, thus forming the signature comet's tail, which can reach as far as 120 million miles."

High, high above the prairies for some weeks that spring of 1910, along with the North Star, the Big Dipper, the Little Dipper, the Milky Way and the millions of twinkling stars there was one bright star in the northeastern sky with a tail somewhat like a dagger. The term "comet" is from a Greek word meaning "long haired." The tail of Halley's Comet is sometimes described as long, flowing hair shaped somewhat like a sword, but that is when the comet is nearing the sun in its race through space, and the tail is becoming longer and longer. But those weeks, that spring of 1910, when Halley's Comet hung in our northeastern sky, the comet was racing *away from* the sun and so the tail was becoming shorter. Even as a small child I had constantly before me the example of my parents taking an objective point of view and striving to meet problems in a practical manner. *Problems of whatever nature were to be solved, or at least modified if at all possible.*

When Halley's Comet came again, in 1986, I understood how marvelous it is for me that I have this remarkable memory of 76 years ago—and that I experienced it with my family.

THERE WERE many excellent factors in my childhood, otherwise I would not have such strong memories of the peace, love and tranquility of our evenings during our years in the sod house. But as I think back and meditate on my growing-up years there must have been some negative factors. May I put it this way: Had life been more ideal I would have been helped to counter my loneliness with ways to entertain myself and to make and keep life interesting, broadening, as well as challenging. Despite my stuttering I conceivably could have found ways to become an intrinsic part of the group, and even to exhibit some leadership characteristics. When I was around twenty my life began to be an adventure, a challenge of experiences. The future had always the possibility of a venture with surprises. My life still is an adventure, in some ways a comedy played out in the theatre of life.

One exceedingly positive and important factor was that I never felt frightened or afraid of life. There was never a more devoted mother than my own dear mother, but the

48

world my brother and I were growing up in was quite a different world from the one my mother grew up in. I have mentioned my loneliness and my restlessness. Freedom to develop my own individual potential became essential to me.

Perhaps the stuttering was in me from the beginning, from the time I learned to talk. I like to think no babe is born to be a stutterer. There must be something to trigger the stuttering. Perhaps those first nine months of crying were enormously significant. My mother, it would seem, observed a dreadful difference in me that caused her to say "Poor little girl."

All in all my parents bequested to me the most noble, the most valuable heritage of all. I could meet problems, uncertainties, hardships; surmount them; and have a happy, rewarding life all the way.

CHAPTER 5

FATHER'S MULES

MONEY! I see money. Much money!'' A small group of gypsies were traveling through the countryside. One of the women looked at my father's palm and told him that. He always said that helped give him courage to buy the mules.

Before the First World War there was unrest in Europe and prices were beginning to go up. Father could not save much money by farming our 160 acres of land, and our sod house was getting old. We needed a bigger home.

In the early twentieth century it was all right for a young family to live in a sod house, but within a few years hardworking, thrifty people ought to be prosperous enough to afford a better home. When western Kansas was being homesteaded, some thirty or so years earlier, families as a matter of course built either a dugout or a sod house. Often after a good frame house was built, the sod house was kept intact and put to some other use.

Father thought he saw a chance to make some money by buying young mules and selling them when they were three years old and were broken to work. My parents discussed the matter. I doubt if my mother would have embarked on such a scheme; perhaps my father was a bit of the dreamer that I am.

Father would go to a farm sale and buy a half-grown, good-looking young mule. The first year he bought only two mules, but he was careful to buy mules that were matched in build and color so that when they were grown he would have a matched pair. I cannot estimate what my father paid for these young mules, possibly $30.00 to $35.00, a price he could manage to pay. We had enough pasture land for them so there was little further expense for these mules until they were three years old. My father always wrote in his record book the date he bought a mule, from whom he bought it and how much he paid for it. He knew each of his mules, so he would speak of "the Smith mule," "the Johnson mule," etc.

There is a special vocabulary that farmers use with their horses and mules. Everyone knows "Whoa" which means stop, stand or hold; "Get up" means start pulling; "Gee" means go right; "Haw" means left. I remember once when I was quite a small child my father was plowing the small area south of our house where the scrub peach trees were. We usually had potatoes planted among those little trees. Or he may have been plowing mother's garden plot which was fenced with five-feet high chicken wire to keep the chickens out of the garden. My father had a walking plow so his hands were on the handles to hold the plow in place and to keep it doing a good piece of work turning over the ground. He was keeping up a steady stream of talking to his horses, directing them with words, not with the reins. Plowing is hard work for man and beast. I still hear my father's voice directing and encouraging his team. "Pansy, Prince, gee." Prince was a big gray horse. Each horse knew its name, as a dog knows its name. "Pansy, haw."

When a pair of mules was nearly three years old, my father would "break" them, that is, accustom the mules to wear harness, to work in the fields, to help pull the farm implements. If a young mule is harnessed and hitched up with steady work horses, he soon learns or becomes accustomed to going along with the steady work horses and pulling his part. It takes a good deal of know-how to break a young horse or mule to work. My mother was fearful where mules were concerned, but my father was always extremely careful and he never had any serious accident during the breaking and working of all those mules.

Mules are stronger than horses, but sometimes not so reliable. They are more practical than stylish. I have read that the bones of a mule are not as fragile as those of a horse. Now, in most parts of the country, one would never see a mule, but in the early twentieth century many farmers had a span of them. A mule is a cross between a mare, that is a female horse, and a donkey. Mules have long ears, often one ear cocked forward and the other back, and they make the "heehaw" sound of a donkey.

When two mules, a matched pair, were fairly well broken, my father would work them together in the field. A matched span of mules do best when worked together all their lives. I have a snapshot of my father driving a fine, sleek span of his matched mules hitched to a lumber wagon. Harold is with him in the wagon, so father was confident of his mules, otherwise he would not have Harold in the wagon.

My father kept on buying young mules. Finally, as the

years went by, he had more mules than he could break himself and work in his fields, so he would "loan" a span of his matched mules to a trusted neighbor who would break the mules and then get a summer of work from them. In the autumn my father would get the mules back and they would be ready to sell.

My father was most careful to whom he loaned his mules, and during the summer he would keep checking to be certain his mules were receiving good care. Ollie Whitney was one neighbor to whom my father loaned a span of mules more than one summer; the Whitney family were our most trusted neighbors. I vaguely remember Grandpa and Grandma Whitney, Ollie's parents. When I was perhaps three years old my parents left me one afternoon with the Whitneys. Ollie who was eighteen years older than I was played with me some that day. I have always remembered him in a very special way.

THERE WAS more excitement around our home after the mule project was well underway, the pace of our lives gradually changed. My parents began to have a different status in the community. Some summers my father had three spans of three-year old mules—the span he was working himself, and the two spans that he loaned to trusted neighbors. Those were busy, challenging years for my parents—surely for Harold and me also.

Before and during World War I our United States army used mules, as did the armies of Europe. That was the reason money could be made on mules at that time. A good span of matched, broken mules sold for $300.00— that was a good bit of money for a western Kansas farmer. My father had some keen insight and a bit of luck in

54

buying and selling his mules. Prices were high and going up. It was a few years before we entered World War I. All in all, over a ten year span, my father must have bought and later sold as matched, broken pairs, two dozen mules, so father had a little money.

GRANDFATHER WHITTEN died when I was nine years old; it seems a pity I have but few memories of him. His 160 acre farm was adjacent to our land on the west. Different farmers rented that farm after grandfather died. My father must have had in mind all the time that he was the one who should buy his father's farm. There was a good frame house and barn that grandfather had built. It was finally settled among the heirs that father was to buy the farm for $4000.00. From the sale of some of his mules my father had a sizeable down payment. He borrowed the rest of the money from his brother-in-law, a retired blacksmith in Lincoln, Nebraska. My father had enough mules growing up to finish the payment in a few years. By the mid-twenties farm prices were down.

By early 1914 we knew we would soon be moving. There was excitement and much anticipation around our home during the months between the time we knew we were to move and our actual move to the Grandpa house. At that time farmers moved the first day of March; that year the first came on Sunday, so we planned to move on Saturday. "It snowed, but we can move anyway," my father decided. The snow was not drifted; it was only a bit more than half a mile from our sod house to the Grandpa house.

My mother was such an efficient planner that the moving of our furniture was accomplished with no problem, and we slept that Saturday night in our new home. My father's part of the moving took longer, for he moved all the outbuildings from the sod house site.

I was thirteen when we moved to our new home—a six-room frame house. I was to have my own room, my very own room.

From that rather desolate spot where our two-room sod house stood, we moved into the house my Grandfather Whitten built some sixteen or so years earlier when he and his family moved from eastern Nebrasksa to Kansas. There were shade trees all around the house, even some trees near the barn and out buildings. There was a pump twenty feet from the kitchen door. How my father must have rejoiced that he no longer had to carry water, two blocks uphill, as he did at the sod house.

A section of land is 640 acres, one square mile. The farm where the sod house stood plus the Grandpa farm gave us a 320 acre farm, half a section of land. Spring Creek ran across the south-west corner of the 160 acres of the Grandpa farm, cutting off three or four acres of land where the house and farm buildings stood. Grandfather had put out a fine orchard of apple and peach trees; there was a splendid row of elm trees all along the west side of our land where the highway ran. Those were tall, elegant, healthy elm trees, for that was before the elm-tree disease ravished them. Also there were cottonwood, box elder, elm and ash trees all along Spring Creek. Grandfather had set out gooseberry bushes and rhubarb plants in the fenced-in garden area. Sometimes in the spring my father would find a slippery-elm tree and bring in a piece of the inner bark which was lovely to chew, far better than chewing gum.

56

(Our currant-picking trips while we lived in the sod house come to my mind. There were currant bushes in the neighbor's pasture just south of our sod house. My father used to go see the owner and get permission for us to pick some of those currants. We knew we would have "chiggers" afterward, but we all went anyway, our dog Die with us of course. We each took a suitable container to hold currants, my father a pail, my mother a big kettle, Harold and I something smaller. We would pick the huge, luscious, ripe, black currants, but also some green currants, so my mother could make jelly from some of them. As soon as we got home we would bathe in soda water and changed some of our clothing. Chiggers, as we called them, are pin-point size red insects that burrow into the skin and make welts that itch and itch. But those currants made such good-tasting jam and jelly! Also it was something of an outing to walk the quarter mile through rather high grass to where the currant bushes grew. We would be ready to go again the next year. After we moved to the Grandpa house we had such an abundance of fruit we didn't bother with the currants.)

SO FROM OUR SOD HOUSE we moved to the most beautiful farm-home setting anywhere around. There were other farm homes along Spring Creek, but none were quite so well situated, all in all, as ours. Our yard was a fairyland of beauty and fragrance when the apple trees were in bloom. Have you seen an apple or peach orchard in full bloom? I have never seen another so lovely as ours was some years; the entire area was fragrant. Nevertheless, no matter how lovely and fragrant they were, those trees had to be sprayed while they were in bloom or each apple would have its worm.

(All summer the trumpet vine in front of the south window of the front room was covered with big, red blooms, elegantly showy and beautiful. After we moved to Phillipsburg we tried repeatedly to get a trumpet vine started beside our house there, but we never succeeded.)

As I think back there were some exquisite experiences we had at the sod house, but that in large measure were lacking at the Granpa farm. I have mentioned the stillness of evening on the prairie, the darkness, the star-filled expanse of sky from horizon to horizon. We seem not to have sat outside evenings at the Grandpa farm. There were often mosquitoes, we were so near the creek, also more bugs and bug sounds. So there was not the same evening silence. The many trees all around made it cooler in summer, but in humid weather cut off any breeze and so made one feel the humidity more. Trees were all around the horizon, thus the night sky was not nearly so vast an expanse. We saw only the stars directly overhead. I now realize something of how great a privilege it was to live on the prairie as we did during our sod house years.

I loved that farm, that land—all 320 acres of it. It was home. No place I have lived since has been the real home that Grandpa house and farm were. Along with that memory I have the remembrance of years of being surrounded with love and protection during our years in the sod house.

HOW DID the mules and our life on the Grandpa farm affect my stuttering? It was a positive factor in my life that my family had more security, but I doubt if that had any real impact on my speech. My stuttering had to do with speaking before people. When I was faced with a difficult speech situation I stuttered. *Circumstances on the farm and in my life someway helped me to develop a resilient personality with latent resources so I could stand on my own two feet.*

MOTHER AND I knew quite well the farm where the sod house stood. Many warm, glowing memories flood my thoughts. There was a small rocky area, not far from our house, where my father used to find Indian arrowheads. That is evidence that Indians roamed that area before it was homesteaded.

In a far corner of the farm sensitive roses grew in another rocky area that could not be farmed. The Stevens book of *Kansas Wild Flowers* gives the name "sensitive brier," the color "rose purple." If one touched the tiny leaflets they curled up and stayed so for perhaps fifteen minutes. In a number of spots in those days one could find wild roses, not roses gone wild, but real wild roses. They were pink with a single row of petals and were very fragrant.

The highway past the Grandpa farm had recently been straightened, so it was a little nearer some of our trees along the creek and north of our house. When we were first at the Grandpa farm, from the road we saw lovely bittersweet growing on one of our trees. We exclaimed over how beautiful that bittersweet was, but we never saw it after that winter. Bittersweet used to be available in florist shops, but I have not seen any for many years.

After we moved to the Grandpa farm it seems I might have explored the area more, but there were mules in the pasture then. Father built up his herd of cattle and some of them had horns. I remember how the bull would sometimes bellow. He had a long, heavy chain in his nose, poor fellow, but otherwise my father would not have been safe near him. Harold would go to bring in the milch cows, but he rode Fanny.

(The book *Kansas Wild Flowers* by William Chase Stevens was not published until 1948, but if I could have had such a book during our last years in the sod house and during our years on the Grandpa farm, and if someone had helped me just a little to get started, I surely would have studied the wealth of wild flowers that were on our farm. We called them weeds. My parents would have been interested and would have encouraged and helped me with collecting and identifying all the wild flowers in the area).

There were wild chokecherry bushes. My mother made the most elegant-tasting chokecherry jelly. Near the Grandpa house there were a few mulberry trees. Those berries are very good to eat right from the tree. My mother mixed them with rhubarb and made excellent jam and butter.

The western half of Kansas was originally covered with buffalo grass. There the rainfall is limited. In a time of drought the buffalo grass dries and turns yellow, but as soon as rain comes it revives and becomes green. Always a short grass, it cures and makes a rich, nutritious layer near the ground. In an early day when the buffalo roamed the prairies, the buffalo in winter would paw the snow away and feed on this rich layer of cured grass under the snow. Thus they could survive the winter in good condition.

A little distance down from the kitchen door was the creek. There was buffalo grass all over our yard. We got a very good croquet set from Montgomery Ward Mail Order House. As many as eight could play, or as few as two. Each time we played we put down the stakes and wire loops because if left in the ground someone might stumble and fall over them. When we had company we usually played croquet. The game requires some skill.

Do you know fireflies? Just the mention of them brings back warm memories of our life on the Grandpa farm, but my mother always said fireflies were an indication of drought. In summer we would often see them in the open area where we played croquet and a little beyond that on a downslope toward the creek. Once I caught a firefly in a jar. It was somewhat amazing to watch it light up in the jar where I could see it well. Then I turned it loose.

REMINISCING about the life of my family in the sod house and on the Grandpa farm sets me dreaming. Could I but relive one hour of those years one choice would be a hot summer evening when we carried our chairs outside and sat on the north side of our sod house. There would be immense joy and peace in hearing my family talking of the day's activities until the dusk deepened into night, and more and more stars twinkled in the vast, clear distance above. Another choice would be with my family during daylight at the Grandpa farm. I would want us to go see the orchard, the barn, the horses, the chickens. Diogenes of course would be with us. I would want to see the woods just north of the house and along the creek. I would want to drink some of the water from the well near the house. If we were near the creek I would be listening for the gurgling sound as the water passed over and among the stones in the place my father used to ford the creek. All the time I would be listening for bird songs. Most of all would be the intense joy of being with my mother, my father, my brother during this hour.

CHAPTER 6

OUR LIFE ON THE GRANDPA FARM

(My Oregon Holly Tree is trimmed. Not just the ends of the branches are cut off, but Mr. White cut many branches off at the trunk so the tree can grow, produce its tiny spicy greenish blooms and bear fine red berries for the Christmas season.)

AFTER ONE and a half years in our new home I was ready for high school. Not nearly all the young people in our neighborhood went on to high school, but it seems it had long been planned that Harold and I should go on. Our farm was eight miles from Phillipsburg so my parents made arrangements for me to stay in town with relatives during the week. The first night away from home I got a mosquito bite on my lip. There I was, an unusually shy and bashful young girl, the first day of high school in a roomful of strange classmates, with a puffed-up lip! (Again my dream memories come to relieve the tension the memory of that mosquito bite brings. The tiny greenish, spicy clusters of holly blooms make the surrounding area fragrant, and they also are nice in a vase in February or March before there are other flowers.)

The rural teachers of course knew my parents: Harold and I rode for two years with one teacher who lived with her parents a few miles beyond our home. Those teachers managed so I was not humbled or humiliated because of my speech, for I haven't much definite memory of stuttering in the one-room school. Also there were only a very few in my class and the lesson periods were quite brief. The other pupils were supposed to be studying their own lessons.

But high school was a different matter. I had four or five different teachers, all new to me. I still vividly recall the anxiety and extreme tension I felt in school, even when it was just a matter of answering the roll call. I would sit there tense from the expectancy of being called on, and that I would have to stutter to get a word or so out. In addition to the anxiety and tension before being called on, after a stuttering incident, there was the feeling of humiliation and subordination that I experienced. Each stuttering incident is a tragedy in the consciousness of the stutterer. Also after a severe stuttering incident there may be some degree of fatigue or exhaustion. Stuttering is very hard work!

The stuttering left me with a feeling of insecurity. That may have begun in the rural school, and certainly there developed in me a strong feeling of insecurity during my high school years. As I think back and meditate that becomes clear. After one has so long lived with insecurity and uncertainty, that very insecurity can seem normal and natural. I have the most hazy but persistent memory that I might look around to see if anyone were snickering over my speech shortcomings. So far as I can recall no one was ever even looking at me. Those teachers were strict. It was an important quality of a good teacher to be strict and so to keep order. This insecurity that I mention seems to have been chiefly in connection with my speech.

I was the only stutterer in that high school of a hundred pupils more or less. No one talked to me about my stuttering, or tried to give me advice. That was a positive factor, for none of them knew what could help me. I think I was never teased about my speech. Latin class was the worst of all for my stuttering—and for me. The teacher was a tense person. I still recall how anxious and tense I was every minute in her room. Such tension was very bad for me and for my speech. That teacher or a teacher in another class would call on me and I would have so much stuttering, maybe on the very first sound, the teacher would say the word for me, and go on to some other pupil. My stuttering was so severe I went through high school with practically no oral recitations, and yet in spite of all my stuttering I enjoyed school and I liked my teachers. I would not have wanted to drop out of school! But one cannot come unscathed through days, weeks, months, really years of such stress.

As I think back I rather marvel. The stress on me was so great it seems it might have made me a nervous wreck. It must have been my parents' love and protection that insulated me so I did not become markedly nervous. On that fine 320 acre farm we felt secure, and then there was my daydreaming. That served as a protection. In a way it also insulated me against damage from circumstances. Now it does not seem to me the high school experience made my stuttering more severe. My speech at home remained the same. The high school classes were just the most difficult speech situations for me that I had ever encountered. My stuttering was there with the same intensity before, during and after the high school years whenever there was a difficult speech situation. One measure of the difficulty of a speech situation was how many people heard me, also how critical the listeners might be.

I suppose my parents didn't realize how serious my speech problem was. The matter of my stuttering, as I recall, was never mentioned in my hearing at home or at school. At home I led an anxiety-free life due to the security, love and devotion my parents gave my brother and me. Most of the time I was completely absorbed in the task at hand, whatever it might be. It was a very small world I moved in.

How did I feel about attending high school? Was my stuttering so embarrassing I would rather have stayed at home? No! Decidedly no! I wanted to go on. It was the thing for me to do to go to high school. My parents were making plans, so of course I went. I'm not certain I had any strong feelings, but it was more interesting to go on to high school. It was challenging and exciting for me to learn new things. You remember I was a lonely child on the farm. Remember also I had always had some repetitions in my speech, so repetitions, stuttering, call it what you will, my speech had always been a part of me, and thus something to live with.

Dr. Wendell Johnson, in his classic small book *Because I Stutter,* 1930, tells of his compensations for the shortcomings in his speech. He excelled in scholarship and in athletics. He made up games with small stones in which his side always won. He wrote poems and articles. These

66

interests kept him in the center of the school activities so he was not an outsider, as I was. It seems I was not very inventive of things to do and of ways to amuse myself. So far as I recall I attempted no compensations. My studious ways were developed early to please my parents. As nearly as I can bring back those adolescent years I was just a contented, happy young person, surrounded by love and care, but it does seem I was often a lonely child and young person. It was at those times I found refuge and comfort in daydreams.

As I look back, it is rather amazing that I seemed to have had no thought of what the stuttering would mean in my later life. I am unable to bring back any associations that shed light on this. As I reflect, it seems probable that such fears were pushed back into the unconscious. In the long run it may be fortunate that I had no plans for the future, that I seemed completely absorbed in the present. If my parents felt anxieties regarding my future they did not communicate them to me, even by muscle tensions. While we lived in the sod house my mother sometimes had a nightmare. A few times I recall I had a nightmare during those years. The stress and anxiety must be quite intense to bring on a nightmare in a young person. I do not recall having any more after we moved to the Grandpa farm. There I had my own room.

Ours was a busy, profitable farm while farm prices were high. My father had sixty or more head of cattle. Every spring there were thirty-five or more new calves. Father did not want to milk but two or three cows, so the calves of the other cows ran with their mothers. They were not weaned for a few months, thus those calves were in excellent condition for fattening and selling, but the farm was a good deal of work for my father who by that time was in his fifties. After we were on the Grandpa farm there seemed to be less anxiety and uncertainty, at least I was aware of less. There were more resources when a drought came. Father had a pit-silo dug. Then in the autumn, or when the corn began to dry up, father would get a man with a silage-cutting machine to fill his pit-silo with cut-up cornstocks. That silage made nutritious feed for the livestock. They liked the silage and kept in excellent condition through the winter.

WHEN I BEGAN attending high school, every Sunday afternoon my father harnessed the horses, and one or both of my parents took me to Phillipsburg, eight miles south of our home. Every Friday afternoon one or both of my parents were in town to do the weekly shopping and to take me home. Then in a couple of years father got a car—a Model T Ford. It cost $400.00. No driver's license was necessary then. If one could keep the motor going and stay on the road, he could drive. The roads then were just dirt, not even gravel. One drove quite fast downhill with the hope that he could get up the next hill on high— not have to shift to low. (In 1968 when I rented a car in England and drove for a week around Wales, my English friend advised me to speed up going downhill so I could easily get up the next hill.) Father learned to drive, then he taught my brother, and finally the same autumn father taught me to drive. It was essential to be able to change a tire on those early cars of 1918, so I learned to change tires.

Those were happy years in the Grandpa house on our 320 acre farm. We all worked hard, my parents on the farm, Harold and I in school. During the summers I read a good deal. My mother had a few books, so I read those. *The Count of Monte Cristo* by Victor Hugo and *Domby and Son* by Dickens. Then there were some library books from the office of the county superintendent—*Black Beauty* and *Little Women*. I would lose myself in a story. I memorized very easily then and I would practice reciting poems before the big mirror in my bedroom. My voice had a youthful quality. My mother once spoke of my voice as being velvety. In reciting those poems I used many inflections and a wide range of pitch. There was no stuttering or substituting words when I recited those poems before my bedroom mirror.

The memory of reciting those poems, it seems to me, was of enormous importance later, even years afterward I always had that somewhat exciting memory of completely free and beautiful speech. Those memories may later have given me assurance there was real help for me if—when I could find it.

IN THAT LOVELY WOODED AREA there surely were many birds and at certain seasons a profusion of bird song, but I seem not to have been much aware of the birds or of their song. You recall the incident of my mother taking me to the pasture to pick wild daisies. I didn't see the daisies until my mother pointed them out to me. I have always been nearsighted.

A nearsighted person may not realize his vision is different from that of other people. He just does not see objects at a distance as distinctly as others do, but he may not know what other people see. He holds his book closer to his eyes than others do. The fine Milwaukee specialist who took care of my eyes for many years once said to me, "You have a wonderful pair of eyes." And that is still true in my late eighties. My cataracts are the slow-growing kind, and the ophthalmologists tell me I shall never need cataract surgery.

So it seems I did not see or hear the birds. I could not see them because I have always been nearsighted. I have no memory of hearing bird songs at that time even though there in the woods along the creek and in our orchard there surely was a profusion of bird song at some seasons. No incident caused me to be particularly aware of their songs. Some years later in Wisconsin I was to become a "birder," but then I had binoculars. During those years I learned to identify many birds by just hearing their song.

At the Grandpa house my bedroom was a room off the front room. To get to my bedroom I went through the dining room and the front room. I felt quite isolated from my family there. Some nights I used to hear a woodpecker drumming on the outside of the house. There must have been grubs in the wall that he was trying to reach. I would lie there petrified with fear, but knowing full well that it was only a woodpecker. I did finally mention the woodpecker to my mother, but I did not speak to her of my fear.

But there was one bird I did see and hear—the wren. A little north and east of our house was the building in which grandfather smoked meat. We called it the Smoke House, but found many other uses for it. Just back of this Smoke House, and hidden from the house, was our outdoor toilet. There were tall trees on the bank just north of that area so it was a pleasant spot. My mother kept an old

70

shoe nailed in an upper corner of the toilet. The wrens regularly nested in that shoe. This was the one bird I did see and hear. The wrens came and went regardless if someone were in the toilet. I learned to recognize the sweet song of those wrens. My mother did not want them disturbed when they were nesting.

There was a profusion of wild life along the creek. Sometimes we saw evidence of beavers working. One winter evening there was a disturbance among the chickens. Father went out, but soon came back in holding up an opossum by its tail. That opossum was playing dead—playing "possum."

ON CLEAR, below-zero, moonlight nights there was often a silence, a quiet that we scarcely know now. There were no radios on western Kansas farms. On such a night we sometimes heard a shrill, squeaking, squealing sound. It was the movement of cold steel contacting icy iron. A quarter of a mile south of our house there was an iron bridge. We always spoke of it as The Iron Bridge for it was unusual then. You know on clear, very cold nights sound carried with amazing clarity. In the years before the First World War Kansas farmers did not have trucks. A farmer hauled his corn, wheat or pigs to market in his lumber wagon pulled by two horses. Often the farmer would walk part of the way beside his wagon to keep warm. He might be returning well after the early-dusk of winter days. There might be snow and ice on the ground and on the bridge.

There were rims of steel around the wagon wheels. The contact of the steel rims on the extremely cold iron of the bridge made sharp, cutting, screeching sounds that

71

carried that quarter of a mile and into our quiet kitchen. After seventy years I still clearly recall those unique sounds. My father might comment that some farmer was returning home. Those sounds continued the thirty seconds or so it took the farmer with his team and wagon to cross the bridge.

I HAD no social life during my high school years, that is no school parties. This was in part because I was a farm child. I was accustomed to being much alone, absorbed in studying for my classes. I was given a little money but I rarely spent any of it. It seemed natural to be much alone, to spend my time studying.

I did have one close friend during my junior and senior years. I had not had a real friend before. Mary looked after her frail and aged grandparents, and attended high school. My mother had known Mary's family years earlier. During my junior and senior years I roomed in Mrs. Murphy's big house just across a side street from Mary. Mrs. Murphy was Mary's great-aunt Sophie. Aunt Sophie had other roomers, but probably because of my mother, she kept an eagle eye on me. Mary and I walked to and from school together, three-fourths of a mile or so. We visited together after school. She milked her grandparent's cow, and did innumerable tasks about her grandparent's home. She cooked the meals. Around the house she often wore an ancient Mother Hubbard worthy of being in the antique collection of a museum. (The Mother Hubbard is the ancestor of the Hawaiian muumuu.) Mary was often up until midnight. My evenings were given over to studying my lessons—in the kitchen of Mrs. Murphy's big house. Nine p.m. was my bedtime.

Mary was a brilliant student and a leader. In a way she was quite pretty with a charm all her own. There was a firm set to her jaw, she moved with a man's stride, and yet she was feminine. Her father was a farmer and a small-town money maker, her mother had the mind and outlook of a business man. Mary spoke with such decision that she influenced people, and most of the time she was correct in her viewpoint. Even the high school teachers listened to her. Mary wanted to take the Manual Arts course; I would have enjoyed taking it too. She did her best to get us admitted to that class but to no avail. The Manual Arts class was for boys only! How fortunate we were to be born in the twentieth century, and not the nineteenth!

Mary certainly was not frivolous any more than I was. She and I talked over things as equals and we discussed everything. Mary did not dominate my thinking, we mutually influenced each other. There was a complete give and take in our discussions. Mary's personality was of a quality to which I could respond with deep friendship. She had more understanding and kindness, greater fullness of spirit and depth than any young person I had met. I could respond to a person with her degree of excellence. Since those years I have rarely been associated with anyone with her keenness of mind.

Quite early in life, even before I learned to read, it seems to me I felt a need for life to be interesting, more challenging than it was for me on our farm. My friendship with Mary certainly made life more interesting, more intense and varied than it had been, but it did not get me into being an integral part of my class. I was still way out on the edge of the group.

I could figure out problems and I could memorize material but I forget quickly. Mary seemed to remember well. One evidence of the brilliance of her mind was she was admitted to the Kansas Medical School. At that time and for many, many years after that it was well nigh impossible for any woman to be admitted to any medical school. After Mary's graduation from medical school she practiced medicine in Phillipsburg. All over that area she was known simply as Dr. Mary. She had a magical smile, and a vigor that was contagious. She was really loved by her patients; she made them feel important. She and I were close friends for many years. Mary seemed stronger than I was, certainly she did more physical work than I did, and lived a more active life; but in her middle years she had a stroke, and died in her sixties. She was a dear, dear friend. Mary was gifted with the ability to see things clearly. The memory of her friendship still has signficance for me.

IT WAS in that high school that I learned to concentrate. There was a large assembly room. During the day it was used as a study hall for pupils when they were not in a class, but sometimes a class met in the front of this large room. I recall one winter when I was a junior or senior, a mathematics class met in the front of that room, but the teacher stood near the back of the room to keep order. I was seated directly in front of where she stood. This teacher had a loud, shrill voice. Sometimes she almost leaned over the seat assigned to me.

I wanted to get work done, I needed to study some of my lessons at that time. It would have been no use to complain to anyone about the situation—besides I liked

Miss Finch and I was far too shy to even think of complaining to anyone. So I did the sensible, logical thing—I learned to concentrate, to shut out that teacher's shrill, piercing voice and to do the assignment for whatever lesson needed to be worked on. I do not think my parents knew anything about this. The ability to shut out sound and to concentrate was a great advantage for me later. Note that this was a problem solved in a most constructive way.

In those days I studied every study-hall period, and every evening, usually in the kitchen of the big house where I roomed. Weekends I studied my lessons at home on the farm. Many present-day teenagers might think that a dull life.

CHAPTER 7

THE DECLAMATORY CONTEST

IT WAS a mild day in February—almost a January-thaw day. After we had the Ford, my mother could go with my father in almost any weather when he went to town. My parents were in Phillipsburg on Friday to do the weekly shopping and to take me home.

As soon as we were out on the highway I said, "There is going to be a High School Delamatory Contest. I want to be in it." There had not been such a contest for five or six years.

"When will the contest be?" my father asked.

Mother's comment was, "We'll have to find a reading for you to give. I wonder if we have any thing that would be suitable."

As I think back over some sixty-five years to 1920, the question did not seem to enter my mind at that time as to how I was going to give a reading when my stuttering was such an ever-present problem in all my class recitations. Certainly I was not exactly facing reality. The rural school and the Sunday School had programs at which the children spoke pieces. I'm certain I took part in those a few years earlier along with the other children. Had I not, I most certainly would remember that!

My mother had had elocution lessons, perhaps what we would now term "Public Speaking." She knew how to give readings. There were special poems my mother practiced reciting to bring out the beauty of her voice, to make her voice full and rich, and to give it carrying power. One such poem was part of Tennyson's "In Memoriam."

Ring out, wild bells, to the wild sky,
 The flying cloud, the frosty light:
 The year is dying in the night;
Ring out, wild bells, and let him die.

As a child I recall being rather amazed at the changes in my mother's voice when I heard her practicing. The quality of her voice with its variations was very different from her everyday speech. Mother used gestures when she gave a reading.

The Women's Christian Temperance Union (W.C.T.U.) occasionally sponsored a declamatory contest. My mother had won a silver medal in the Matrons' Declamatory Contest, and later she won a gold medal. My father, Harold and I were ever so proud of mother. We believed in her and took it more or less for granted that she would win. When we dressed up I liked mother to wear one of her medals.

There were also declamatory contests for young people. I have a silver medal that I won in such a contest. I seem to remember almost nothing about that contest, but I do have the medal to show I won it. That was in my early teens. It was just a local neighborhood contest sponsored by the W.C.T.U. There were only three or four of us who took part in that contest. My mother helped select the piece I gave, and taught me how to give it. She did exercises with me to get my voice so it would carry well, also exercises to make my voice rich and full. So a few years earlier I was accustomed to taking part in activities where there was speaking and I was accustomed to doing well.

My mother helped me select a reading for the high school contest, and I began to memorize it. The following weekend she was going to hear me say the part I had memorized and help me work out the best way to deliver it. That was Friday evening after supper. The kerosene lamp was lighted. My mother was tired after a busy day. We did not begin with exercises to give my voice fulness and to increase its carrying power. I was just saying the part I had begun to memorize. There was a good deal of stuttering.

Finally my mother gently said, "Oh, you can't do it, Dear Heart." There was certainty in my mother's voice. "Dear Heart" was a very special term of endearment. Once when I was quite ill, while we lived in the sod house, my mother used that term of endearment, Dear Heart. Mother was only saying the obvious thing. Certainly I could not stutter that much in a declamatory contest— I could not stutter at all in a declamatory contest.

I still feel some of the challenge I felt than. I wanted to be in that contest. I didn't say anything, at least not much. There was nothing to say. I was determined to be in that contest. To give up was not in my make up. As I think back I feel more than amazement, for I was such a shy, bashful young person. I feel humbled by the spirit I showed then. As I write this it is difficult for me to understand the strength I showed at that time. I try to see myself objectively as I was then. There was a vigor, a determination in my makeup that led me on. Remember I was somewhat on my own after age fifteen because it was necessary for me to stay in Phillipsburg during the week while I attended high school. As I think back it seems to me my parents wanted my brother and me to be able to make decisions that we would want to live by.

As I try to analyze what factors were operative it seems important that in my own estimation I was accustomed to being something of a winner, that is a winner in my own small world. When my brother was nine, father got him a 22-rifle. Then Harold, father and I practiced a good deal of target shooting, so I learned to be an excellent shot. My nerves were steady and I was persistent in my efforts to learn. When father got his first Model-T Ford, father, Harold and I learned to drive. I even learned to change tires. My mother was an excellent cook. She helped me learn to bake cakes. In a way all of this was being a winner.

In high school there was more competition, but I was still one of the very best students. I was one of the very best because I tried so very hard. At the beginning of my third year it occurred to me to try especially to see how well I could do in all my subjects. My grades were really high after that. It gave me the highest degree of pleasure, of joy, to do a thing well.

My problem was to work out a way I could recite the reading we had selected. I knew my mother would be with me all the way. At the Grandpa farm there was a big barn with stalls at each end for horses, or cows, and a center high section for hay. When my father filled that section with alfalfa the entire area around the barn was fragrant. When the central section, the haymow part, was partly empty there was much open space, a good place for me to practice voice exercises and part of my reading. If afforded a far larger area than any part of the house. So weekends I practiced out in the barn. To say lines such as "Ring out, wild bells—," and to fill a large area such as a barn or an auditorium with sound, one must speak in quite a different way from ordinary conversational speech. This was an important element in my giving my reading. Also it was a bit like playing a part in a play, as being a character in a drama.

My mother sometimes used James Henry Leigh Hunt's "Abou Ben Adhem" for practice, so I used that, too.

> Abou Ben Adhem (may his tribe increase)
> Awoke one night from a deep dream of peace,
> And saw, within the moonlight in his room,
> Making it rich, and like a lily in bloom,
> An Angel writing in a book of gold:

I also needed to practice during the week. At Mrs. Murphy's house, where I roomed, there was a big empty barn—a huge barn. Possibly my father thought of my practicing in that barn, possibly I thought of it. Anyway it was worked out. Mrs. Murphy was willing. Every afternoon after school I bundled up and went out to practice my vocal exercises and my reading in that huge, semi-dark barn. It was early spring. The barn was cold, so my voice came out rich and vibrant when I practiced. (The original owners of Mrs. Murphy's big house, around the turn of the century before automobiles, must have kept a span of horses and carriage, perhaps even a riding horse.)

One can speculate as to what the teachers thought when I was going to be in that declamatory contest. It was as though I lived two existences—the moments when I was called on to recite and stuttered severely, and the rest of my life when I had very little speech difficulty.

I was not very realistic, that spring of 1920, one may say, but I shudder to think what a limited life I might have had if I had given up. That declamatory contest time was a turning point in my life. I accepted responsibility for how I would deliver my reading. If you read this in a novel, you would think it could not have been. I proved myself, at least for the time being, to be the master of my own fate. In a way this matter of the declamatory contest forecast what would be the outcome when fifteen years later I was to go to Iowa to work on my stuttering. If this were a play, a drama, this declamatory contest would be the first indication of how the play would end, of what the final scene might be. Not of *how* I would overcome the stuttering problem, but that someway it would be got under some control so that I could go on to a successful professional life.

The voice exercises produced more variety in pitch and more diaphragm support, thus greater vigor and more variations in my speech sounds. Those voice exercises gave me a way of speaking which was far different from an-swering a question in class. Also, remember, I had the memory from a few years earlier of reciting poems before my bedroom mirror with beautiful, free speech.

The only help I had in preparation for the declamatory

82

contest was from my mother. She spoke of good posture, also of projecting my voice so I would be clearly understood and of using variations in pitch to make my voice full and resonant. There was no mention of how I should breathe. I am firmly of the belief that in dealing with stuttering the breathing should in no way be involved. I practiced very consistently every afternoon after school for a half hour or so. I worked as carefully as I knew how. My aim in the declamatory contest was to do my best—my very best. I had little thought of whether there was a possibility I could win the contest; my intent was just to do my best.

I have pondered a good deal as to why I wanted to be in that contest—why I was determined to be in it. I knew what such contests were. It was challenging and I gloried in things that were fairly difficult, in things that not everyone could do. It gave me immense satisfaction to do a thing well. That spring the vision that I was doing my reading well was sufficient to keep me trying all the more. The contest certainly made that spring of 1920 more interesting for me and for my parents.

My practicing went on for six weeks or possibly two months. Of course there were also school lessons to do. It was at this time I realized that physically there were limits as to what I could do. I suppose I became quite tired after a day in school followed by a session of practicing in the big, old barn. I must have felt more stress because of the contest.

My mother was helping me every weekend, so she no doubt realized I was doing very well. A few days before the contest my father promised me a ring if I won. I distinctly recall the quality of his voice, not his exact words. He had confidence in my ability, but I couldn't work any harder than I was working and trying. I don't think the promise of the ring made any difference in the effort I put into the preparation for the declamatory contest. As I reflect, it was chiefly my father's voicing of his assurance that he was back of me in all ways. My mother was also. She helped me with the delivery—she always, always helped me in every way she could.

The contest was held in the space used as a gymnasium and also as an auditorium. There was no sound amplification system in 1920, but I was accustomed to filling that big, old, cool, empty barn with rich, vibrant sound. It was spring so the room was comfortably cool, thus sound carried well. Only the stage was lighted for the contest, but I knew where my parents were seated. Mrs. Murphy was with them, she was proud of me, too. We contestants were seated on the stage. I do not recall any distinct feeling during the contest and while we waited for the decision of the judges. I had delivered my reading just as my mother had shown me and as I had practiced it every afternoon for weeks in the big, cool, semi-dark barn. I felt complete confidence and security in my mother's judgment. After a brief interval the superintendent came out on the stage. Ida Whitten was the winner of the Phillipsburg High School Declamatory Contest.

Then a few weeks later there was the County Declamatory Contest. As one young man was giving his declamation I realized his delivery was better than mine, so I could not feel badly that he won first place. I was second place.

A few weeks after the contest, my father, mother and I went into the jewelry store—there was only one in town. The jeweler, a middle-aged German, set out a tray of medium-priced rings. One was a gold ring with a small opal. I thought that the prettiest ring I had ever seen. I still have the ring and I wear it with remembrance of my parents and with pride.

You may wonder how I felt about my stuttering at that time. I cannot recapture any very strong feeling. It certainly was a relief to have a bit freer speech, but the stuttering was still there. When I did stutter I was helpless as ever. The improvement was merely a decrease in the frequency and duration of the stuttering incidents. I felt less like a stutterer, and that was assuredly a positive factor, but *a reduction in the frequency and duration of stuttering incidents is not sufficient to rescue an adult stutterer.* I did not realize it then, but what I really needed was some way of meeting a stuttering moment and of being able to deal with it in conversational speech. It would be fifteen years before I would find such a means of helping myself. *I also needed to be able to meet life situations more adequately, to enter more fully into all the possibilities life offers.*

It is more than sixty-five years after the declamatory contest that I am writing this account. Recently I came upon a paper I wrote in 1937, nearly twenty years after the contest. That paper has this sentence: "I feared and hated stuttering then, as all stutterers do." That is not at all true for me now. I neither fear nor hate stuttering. Hate is a crippling thing. It is only through action that there can be victory.

After the declamatory contest there were still a few weeks of school. I have written of our beautiful farm. I recall well, our class was planning a picnic. I stood up by my seat, described a little about our farm, and invited the class there for the picnic. The class did not accept my invitation, and it was just as well for they wanted a place where there were tables and benches, but it did something for me to be able to stand up and invite them. My invitation was an effort to become an integral part of the group—my class.

So after the declamatory contest my speech was a little better in school. I felt somewhat more adequate. I had brought honor to our class. I was also Salutatorian. On graduation evening I was to give a short speech. I was somewhat fearful. During the declamatory contest the auditorium was in darkness, only the stage was lighted. So in the contest I was really playing a part in a drama. On graduation night the lights would be on in the auditorium as well as on the stage. I would be speaking for myself. As I think back it seems I should have been able to work out a delivery with which I would have felt secure, as I did in the declamatory contest. I did have a slight amount of difficulty with stuttering during the delivery of the Salutatorian speech. When a stuttering incident came I was helpless and humbled.

CHAPTER 8

TEACHING A RURAL SCHOOL

AS NEARLY AS I can recall during my last year of high
school I was giving little thought as to what I was
going to do after graduation. It seems I was completely
absorbed in my school classes and the declamatory contest.
Now that seems strange to me. Was I blocking out thoughts
of the future because of fear? True, it was pleasant being
home with my family on our beautiful farm. What could
a stuttering girl do?

An exceedingly faint memory finally comes to me that
early in the spring my parents had mentioned that I might
teach a rural school. At that time I spoke of Red Top, our
local school. The thought in my mind was that thus I
could live at home with my family. But my parents did
not think Red Top a good idea.

Sometimes, before radio and television, people just sat
evenings, resting from the day's labor. Often there was
little conversation. I distinctly recall one evening, a Friday
or Saturday evening for I was home, we were sitting in

our quiet kitchen after supper. It was spring so we didn't need to sit quite near the stove for warmth.

"German children mind their parents and they will mind a teacher. A school in a German neighborhood will be best." I still distinctly hear my father's voice. He had been thinking. He grew up in a German community. As my father saw the situation the normal thing was for his daughter to teach a rural school. I was surprised at my father's words. I had not been thinking seriously of teaching a rural school—or of the future! I just kept silent.

Since my mother had been a teacher, she knew the problems. It seems to me my father planned a rural teaching position for me, and I just accepted the plan. Of course my parents had talked the matter over, but my father I feel certain was the moving force. He made some inquiries.

West of Phillipsburg there was a large, prosperous German settlement with several German Lutheran churches in which services were conducted in German. Just west of that was a large Dutch settlement. My father made more inquiries, then one fine Saturday in May he took me with him in the Ford, and we set forth to interview school board members of a rural school west of Phillipsburg. The varied odors of cattle farms, many with orchards, were in the air. Freshly turned earth has a special fragrance. Everywhere there was the odor of recently plowed fields and growing plants. The country-side was at its best. We went to see the three school board members. All were rugged, big-scale farmers, men who knew crops, farm animals, and also drought, as my father did.

"Her mother was a teacher. She can teach." Father

did the talking and spoke with assurance. I still hear his voice saying those words.

In 1920 prices were still high after World War I. Teachers were scarce. I was hired to teach Silver Light School for a seven-month term at $100.00 per month, an excellent salary for a rural teacher.

Before I could teach I had to secure a teacher's certificate. The county superintendent could give out sets of questions used in earlier teachers' examinations. Even though I was an excellent student those teachers' examination questions were quite difficult. So I studied from those questions. I studied for hours each day. Week after week I studied. My mother would not let me help her much during those weeks. She wanted me to study for she knew how difficult those teachers examinations could be. She wanted me to pass them, to pass with high grades. In August I wrote the two days of teachers' examinations, and did get the needed certificate.

MRS. FRITCH, a small, kind, elderly widow, lived an eighth of a mile west of the school. I roomed and boarded at her home. Her front room was decorated with four framed hair-wreaths. The hair, from some of her deceased dear ones, was twisted into flower-shapes to form wreaths. Mrs. Fritch was a true gardener so we had a variety of vegetables to eat.

Every Sunday afternoon my parents took me to Mrs. Fritch's house, every Friday at four they were there to take me home. In fine weather it was a pleasant ride. That school was seventeen miles from our farm. Of course my parents stopped in Phillipsburg on Fridays to do the shopping, but seventeen miles, a round trip of thirty-four miles, was quite a distance for the Ford. There were just dirt roads, not even gravel. As I recall father drove twenty, sometimes thirty, miles per hour. At that time forty miles per hour was quite fast and used more gas.

There were sixteen lively pupils in the eight grades. Half of the children understood and spoke German. One shy little seven-year-old girl did not understand any English. In school one of the pupils who knew German would help her some. At home, August, her fine big brother, would teach her. Her parents began speaking English to her. It was surprising, but within a month she was getting along all right in first grade.

The parents of the sixteen pupils were cooperative and wanted their children to learn. I had very little stuttering so my speech was no problem. I liked the children and their parents, and I enjoyed the teaching. The young people in the community included me in their parties. That was the first time I had any social life apart from school.

The next spring father found another school that was only twelve miles from home. He took me to interview the three members of that school board. Again he did the talking. I taught Pleasant College School the next two years. That was an even more prosperous community. The land was a little more level and the German people seemed to know how to keep the land fertile. All save one family were German, but all of us were staunch Americans!

Again the summers of 1921 and 1922 I had to take two days of teachers examinations to get a new teachers' certificate. That meant weeeks of study before the examination to be certain I could pass—pass with high grades.

90

The winter of 1921-22 I roomed at the Grau home, a white house on a hill. The barn and out-buildings were red. Mr. and Mrs. Grau had come over from Germany many years earlier, but they spoke practically no English. Katie, the daughter, kept the house spick and span and cooked excellent meals. She canned many foods for winter. Mrs. Grau knit beautiful, warm mittens out of fine wool yarn. There was an elaborate pattern on the back of the hand. I liked to try everything, so I bought some fine wool yarn. Katie translated her mother's directions and before the coldest weather came the mittens were finished and I was wearing them. But I never wanted to knit any more mittens—it was too complicated and monotonous.

I did two things in that small rural school that were innovative, and largely solutions to problems I saw. The school desks did not fit the small children. My father helped me and we nailed together the ends of wooden orange crates to make footstools. (At that time orange crates were made of wood.) With these nailed-together ends of orange crates, the smaller children had a solid base for their feet, their legs did not have to dangle in mid-air all day!

The old one-room rural schools have been somewhat idealized, but in cold weather pupils needed to sit near the heating stove to be comfortable. Pupils carried their noon lunches in tin lunch pails. These lunch pails were left in the cloak hall or during the coldest weather might be kept on the floor under the pupil's desk. But even there the lunches sometimes froze.

I bought a large aluminum kettle with a bail across the top so it was easy to carry. I think that cost one dollar then. This was to be a soup kettle. I talked the matter over with some of the parents, and sent word home with the children to the others. The children drew names and we had hot soup three times per week during the cold months. I took the first turn. My mother made the soup and I brought it from home. Thus my turn came on a Monday. It was often chicken soup with vegetables added.

The stove that heated the school was an old-fashioned coal stove, perhaps four feet high. A half-hour before lunch, I would set the soup kettle on top of the stove so the soup would be bubbling hot for our lunch. The odor of the soup whetted our appetites. Every kettle of soup tasted excellent! On soup-days each child brought a spoon and a cup or dish to eat the soup from. I, the teacher, took a big spoon on soup-days and dished out the soup for each child. Then I would send the soup kettle home with the child whose turn it was to bring the soup the next time.

The parents and I both felt the children came through the winter better with our hot-lunch program. Certainly hot soup was better than a half-frozen lunch. The children did better school work, too. The parents appreciated that I was helping their children. No other rural school around had footstools or a hot lunch program. This was original thinking and planning on my part—of course my own parents helped with my planning.

I recall I sometimes had a little difficulty pronouncing the spelling words. I might stutter on words beginning with a plosive sound—P or B, T or D, K or G. Once I was having three spelling lessons at one period when one of the mothers came in to visit. The children were to write the spelling words. If I pronounced each word quite loud and clear, I could get the words out without stuttering. In speaking louder I was using a different voice.

TWO OF MY FATHER'S SISTERS lived in Lincoln, Nebraska. They urged me to visit them, so the summer of 1922 I did. I think I intended to stay two weeks, but when I got there I registered for a summer school class at the university. Some of my Lincoln cousins were attending college. The class I registered for was ''Elocution—Reading and Speaking.'' But I had learned public speaking from my mother. There was a slight stuttering problem. I earned two credits with a grade of 91. Thus I learned the lay of the city of Lincoln, how and where some of the street cars ran. Everything about the city was new and wonderful to me, even the rattle and rumble of the street cars, strange people on the streets, big department stores. I learned the plan of the university grounds. I began to feel the contagious urge of students to do well, to achieve. After I returned home I again had to study before I took the two days of teachers' examinations to renew my teaching certificate.

Toward the end of that summer I had an attack of what we called rheumatism. My right shoulder, my left hip and my left ankle were the parts most affected. The doctor in Phillipsburg was not much help. No definite diagnosis was made. My heart seems not to have been affected. Finally my parents took me to Waconda Springs, a hundred miles east of home, where I had bath treatments. It was a place similar to well-known Excelsior Springs, Missouri, only on a far smaller scale. So I was recovering. The opening of school was postponed one week.

93

Katie Grau was married during the summer, so I was to room in the Dieckhoff home that winter of 1922-23. My father took Fanny, our treasured saddle horse, over to the Dieckhoff farm. Mr. Dieckhoff took care of her as though she were his own. Our dear Fanny. I rode her to school for two weeks. While I had Fanny there I decided to make home calls on the pupils after school, so I was in each pupil's home.

The Dieckhoff farm and house have a history. Mrs. Dieckhoff's parents, Mr. and Mrs. Veeh, homesteaded the farm in 1871. They came to Kansas from Minnesota, but they were of German ancestry. Their first home was a dugout with a sod roof. In 1895 they put up an eleven room house, built entirely of oak. The roomy barn was also built mostly of oak. That splendid house still stands, a show place, a house similar to an old colonial mansion.

The buffalo no longer roamed the prairies by 1871, but there were a few stories of peaceful Indians. Once as a small group of Indians went through the area, one of their infants died. The Indians wrapped the little body in a blanket and left it in a tree to be picked up on their return trip. Some of the settlers found the small corpse and gave it proper burial in the ground. On their return the Indians were pacified when the burial was located. According to their tribal ritual it was necessary for them to take the little body to their tribal burying grounds.

I WOULD most certainly prefer to skip the relating of my aches and pains, however if my case of stuttering is to be fully understood, all this must be told. The spring of 1923 I suddenly became ill one afternoon in school. I dismissed the children, and someway got to the Dieckhoff home

94

and telephoned my parents. They came for me as speedily as was at all possible. The minutes seemed hours as I waited for them. I doubt if aspirin was widely used then, at least I didn't have any medicine at all to take. At some moments I was in a cold sweat from the torture I was undergoing, then hot all over and trembling. The pain persisted minute after minute, hour after hour. Then my parents came. The jolting and shaking during the six mile car ride to Phillipsburg increased my anguish and torment. We went to the doctor's office and he gave me a hypodermic injection for the pain. Then slowly, gently blessed relaxation and relief. That evening I seemed perfectly all right, no diagnosis was made as to what had caused the pain. X rays nearly twenty years later revealed eight small gall stones, and thus explained the intense pain of 1923. I never had any other gall stone attack, but sometimes my skin would be rather yellow and I would not feel well. In 1941 I finally had gall bladder surgery. After that my health was better and I was stronger than I had ever been before.

I ENJOYED the children during those three years of rural teaching. Every Christmas I get letters from some of them, men and women, now retirement age. Those children were closer to me than any pupils I had in later years. I enjoyed parties given by the young people in the neighborhood where I taught. My parents would have been willing for me to marry. Even at that time marriage was still held to be essential for a girl. No fate could be much worse than to be an old maid! But I did not want to be a farm wife as my mother had been. I wanted to go to college. There was a sort of wanderlust in me, a daring that my mother could not quite understand, a love of adventure such as I read of in books. Perhaps my father gloried more in my willingness to venture, to try new things.

In a way those three years of rural teaching were marking time. There was nothing very challenging for me in that life. I seem not to have read any books during those years. The last winter of my rural teaching I did subscribe to one monthly publication—a fitness magazine with emphasis on exercise and diet. I had saved a little money. I wanted to go to college the autumn of 1923. This was my own decision—no one encouraged me unless it was Mary, my high school chum. She went on to college from high school.

As I reread and ponder over this chapter it seems not very interesting. Perhaps that is because my life was not very challenging during those three years. My loneliness as a child, and my aloneness as a young person may have led me to set up criteria, conditions, so to speak, for my future. Life must be interesting, challenging, rewarding, and at all events in the end practical, also to some degree successful. If life might have an element of adventure that made it even better. It seems there was a great idealism in me. The ideal, the need was to learn more, to understand and comprehend more and still more, to expand and push out the restricting walls of the so-small world I knew.

CHAPTER 9

1923–1931

MY PARENTS finally arranged for me to stay with old friends of our family who then lived in Lincoln, Nebraska. It was easy to get to Lincoln for the Rock Island Railroad went through Phillipsburg, then directly to Lincoln and on to Chicago. So I attended the University of Nebraska for two years. It was good to compete in a large university—sink or swim.

I had gone through high school with a minimum of oral recitation, and so it was in college. There was one older Latin professor, Dr. Stanford, whom I liked. He was kind and gentle, but I stuttered severely in his class anyway. I had a mental set, one might say, to stutter on the Latin. I had always stuttered on the Latin, I anticipated stuttering, I was somewhat tense before I was called on, I was a bit tense even before the class began. But that is what stuttering is!

A cousin and I were in some classes together. Since I have been writing this account, a memory has come to me. This cousin was sometimes embarrassed by my stuttering. Once she said "Can't you talk?" Norman Howe, whom I have mentioned as having a slight stutter all his life, was her brother, so it would seem she might have had a more sympathetic reaction for a stutterer's feelings. A stutterer stutters only because at that moment he cannot speak any other way. It was so deep a hurt it was forgotten, that is, it was pushed back into the unconscious. I cannot altogether blame my cousin, however, for stuttering can be nearly as disturbing to the listener as to the stutterer.

But even with my stuttering as a hindrance, those college years brought growth, insights and a broadening of horizons. Someway I knew to get my classes with experienced professors, men of insight and vision, who were also kind and gentle. It was a time of growth for my spirit. It seems this should have come earlier for me on our beautiful farm with the woods, the birds, the wild flowers and my loving parents. I majored in English Literature. I was something of a dreamer, I could lose myself in a story. There was one course that may have influenced me in later years. That course was Logic, offered by the Philosophy Department. I made a grade of 90 in the course. When the need came some ten years later that course may have enabled me to reason out things somewhat more logically and realistically than I might otherwise have done.

It was still a small world I lived in, but I did win honors, one each year. In freshman English, of course, we wrote themes. My professor deemed one of mine worthy of putting in a small magazine he was editing. It was a story inspired by seeing a statue of Lincoln at the new state Capitol Building.

In my second year I was in an archery class instead of the regular gym class. I enjoyed the archery and I sometimes went out on the field for extra practice. Then you remember I had learned to be an excellent shot with my brother's 22-rifle. At the end of the year there was an archery contest. I wanted to do well in the contest, but as I think back, I'm not even sure I thought I had a chance of winning. Certainly there was nothing like the determination and effort that went into the winning of the declamatory contest five years earlier.

"Swish, ping! Swish, ping!" We shot at three distances. This was the last and shortest—thirty feet. Up to that time my score was good, but not spectacular. Now every one of my arrows was hitting the target. Toward the end of the contest a photographer was there, but he was taking pictures only of some of the sorority girls. His presence caused me to shoot each arrow with special care.

"Swish, ping!" Swish is the sound the feathers on the sides of the arrow make as the arrow leaves the bow, ping is the sound as the arrow pierces the target. Even though my excitement was high, that did not deter my steady arm and exact eye focus. My arrows kept on piercing the target, many right in the Bull's Eye. Perhaps it was not even a very close contest. Anyway I won. The evening paper, at the very bottom of the front page, had a three or four line item stating that Ida Whitten won the Archery Contest.

That was the spring of 1925. I was twenty-three years old. I still hear the "Swish, ping!" of sixty-four years ago. "Swish, ping! Ping! Ping! Swish, ping!"

You, the reader, may ask what this archery contest story has to do with my stuttering, or the footstools and the hot lunch program during my rural teaching. It is my belief that any and every incident in a stutterer's life may influence his stuttering. It may be difficult to measure the effect, but I am firmly convinced that is true. Through the footstools and the hot lunch program I stood higher in the estimation of the pupils and their parents. That caused me to feel better about myself than I might have otherwise. Those incidents gave me more confidence in my ability to do things—to attempt new action. For me it was pioneering in problem solving. Within ten years I was to need all the courage, all the initiative, all the imagination, all the peseverance I could muster to meet the problem of my stuttering.

The story of a first grade girl I later worked with in Racine, Wisconsin, comes to my mind. Mary was a charming little girl with a good deal of originality. Her parents were middle-class people who owned their home and seemed secure. There was a sister two or three years older. Mary had an obvious stutter, but it was not so severe stuttering as some. I suggested the mother keep a Diary. This Diary would be for her use, never for me to see. I suggested she put all manner of incident in it: parties, weather, food, any and every kind of detail. She could make entries several different times during the course of a day. Mary's first grade teacher was an experienced person with a daughter of her own. She may not have listened much to me though. A child should never be held back in school because of stuttering.

First grade teachers may have three or even four reading sections, divided according to ability and achievement. Mary's teacher had three groups with bird names. Bluebirds were the best readers, then robins and orioles. The scarcity of bluebirds may add to the charm associated with their name. Their song is soft and sweet. So, much as we enjoy

100

our robins, most children might choose to be bluebirds, especially if the teacher makes that name attractive.

Mary no doubt knew she was in the second-best group. She probably realized she read as well as the ones in the bluebird group. Why was she not with the bluebirds? This was an unasked, unanswered question, but evidently a matter that troubled Mary. Toward spring there was a Standardized Test that all first graders took. Mary scored very high on that test, so high that her teacher felt she had no choice but to put Mary in the bluebird section.

How did this affect Mary's stuttering? Her stuttering disappeared. We cannot know how events may affect an individual or his stuttering. It seems to me safe to assume that any event which leaves a definite impression or memory in the mind of the stutterer may have an influence on the stuttering. There seemed to be no stuttering at all in Mary's speech over a period of time, more than a year. Hopefully the family had learned better how to deal with Mary and her speech. The parents felt she no longer needed even to have her speech watched. So far as I ever knew there was no recurrence of Mary's stuttering.

In 1924 my parents moved to Phillipsburg. Their house there was to be home for fifty years, but the place I loved was the farm. When my father realized that my brother was not going to want to live on the farm, father wanted to move to town. He had grown up in a family of ten children. The farm must have been just too lonely when both his children were gone, and then my parents saw the financial indications. The First World War had ended a few years earlier. A few years later a number of our former farm neighbors lost their farms during the depression years, but our 320 acre farm never had a mortgage after the purchase loan was repaid.

The house in Phillipsburg had electricity. It was connected with the city water but we had only a cold-water faucet until almost twenty-five years later. After World War Two father put in a bathroom and a hot water heater. That was luxury for us. In spring the spirea around our front porch made our humble home a small palace of fragrance, grace and beauty. Then there were lilacs south of the house, and in the back yard two huge locust trees that replaced the elms killed by the elm-tree disease.

THE AUTUMN of 1925 I went to teach English in the high school at Imperial, Nebraska. The University Placement Bureau notified me of the vacancy. I sent a written application, and was hired without a personal interview. My speech problem seemed slight during the two years I taught there. It was no real handicap. The superintendent-coach was impressed that I had won the archery contest the spring before. He had me demonstrate before his athletes just how to hold the bow and arrow. They asked a few questions about how to aim, etc. One must hold the bow correctly or one's left wrist will be grazed and become sore.

Imperial is in the southwestern part of the state, at the end of a branch railway line. That area is a good deal more western than around Phillipsburg. There are sandhills and sagebrush not far outside the town. And rattlesnakes. I still have the rattle from a big rattler. The South Divide with its level, fertile land and rich farmers was a few miles away. The sandhill people managed as they could. There is great beauty of a very special kind in the sandhill canyon country, a beauty somewhat mingled with mystery. The best time to see the canyons is in the evening before twilight. I could dream dreams there. It was always a real treat to be invited for a drive into the canyon country. And there are sandstorms! Sometimes one cannot see beyond the radiator.

During my two years at Imperial I had more social life than I had ever had before. I made life-long friends there, men and women. A dozen of the young women in Imperial organized a Bridge Club. We had pleasant times together, and bridge is an interesting pastime, but I needed something deeper, more fundamental to living. Now in my retirement years, I say I do not have time for bridge. I have written of being outside my peer group during my high school years. Then in Imperial I was nearer to being an integral part of a social group than I had ever been before.

Something was leading me on, not driving me, but beckoning me on. As I think back I only vaguely understood why I wanted to leave Imperial and go back to the university. Even then when I was twenty-five Imperial did not offer the depth of experience, the adventure I needed, or so it seemed. I wanted to be where there were more educational and cultural challenges and advantages. In a way college for me was an adventure in new fields, certainly it was an opening of vistas. I had started my college course, so I had a feeling I should finish it and get my degree. There was a restlessness in me that persisted for many years, a striving for something my life lacked. (The thought and reflection that go into the writing of this story, this account, stir depths and emotions I had not been aware of in my quiet retirement here in San Diego!

It relieves some of the tension I feel even yet in discussing my stuttering to recall the tiny Anna's hummingbird singing outside my glass doors. On hot days he sits on a cord over my terrace and sings his little scratchy, squeaky, grating, high-pitched song. The Anna's is the only hummingbird in the United States that sings. As he sits and sings he wiggles. He must have vermin on him that he wiggles so. He sits there only on very warm days, then he is there for several hours. There is always a light breeze across my terrace. The Audubon Guide describes his song as a "jumble of squeaks, gurgling and hissing notes.")

Since I had not much difficulty with stuttering while teaching in the rural schools near Phillipsburg, or in the high school in southwestern Nebraska, it might seem I should have continued there. But when I was on the spot, so to speak, during teaching, in social life, or at the university the stuttering was there in full force. I had no aggressive way of meeting a stuttering incident. I do not think there was any way I could have lived securely with my stuttering even slight as it seemed at times. To escape high blood pressure and tension any individual needs to feel secure. The analogy that comes to my mind is how would it be to live with a family of rattlesnakes under the porch of one's house! I did not realize it then, but now as I look back over the years it seems that ever since my elementary school days I was simply marking time before there had to be a confrontation with the fact of the presence of the stuttering in me. What I needed was a way of successfully meeting a stuttering incident and changing it into something acceptable. Also something that would relieve the stress, the tension that floods over the stutterer when he has a block. I know now these are realistic hopes for an adult stutterer. (Again the scratchy squeaks and gurgles of the hummingbird tend to relieve my remembrance of tensions. Once I found a hummingbird nest outside a window where I was living. Two navy-bean sized eggs were in it, extra small navy-bean size those two eggs were.) The incident of the declamatory contest did a great service for me, but it was not the final solution—nor was there anything I could have done to make it such. One comes to appreciate the ability to speak, to express oneself, a precious privilege that others have always known.

The autumn of 1927 I was back at the University of Nebraska. I had attended several summer school sessions so I had enough credits to graduate the spring of 1928. After graduation I taught one year in a small high school near Lincoln, then I had the opportunity to teach at the State Teachers College at Aberdeen, South Dakota. I was hired to take the place of a teacher who wanted a leave of absence. It was a cultural advance for me to teach at a college where some of the teachers were privileged individuals. Mrs. Garvin spoke French and German, and picked up Spanish when she was going to Spain on a trip. She had studied abroad and traveled widely in Europe. She was much older than I was, but we became close friends. Association with her helped to broaden my horizons; a desire to travel was born in me.

There were other teachers, all older, whose friendship came to mean a good deal to me. The social life was of a quality I had not known before. Many of the college teachers were sensitive, caring people. I was in the group, a little on the edge, but definitely in that warm friendly group of teachers. Some showed me real kindness and consideration. One small incident was a car ride to hunt

the Pasque flower. We found it blooming in the snow.
"The Pasque" was the name of the school annual. There
were cultural experiences, music and art, that enlarged
my view—a good library. One winter I read several volumes
of plays, one the plays of George Bernard Shaw.

As a College teacher I had more responsibility. The
teaching of older, more mature students increased the stress
on me. The severity of my stuttering increased. Some of
my students were very bright young people. I had only
an A.B. Degree at that time. I think I should not have
been teaching college seniors. Also the teacher whose place
I was taking wanted to return to the college.

After the summer session my brother came in his car
to take me home. We went on a camping trip through
the Black Hills. Mount Rushmore Memorial was being
carved out then—chiseled out. That was 1931. The first
day we got a late start. Most cars were not air conditioned
then. It was so warm driving west across South Dakota
that my face was a little burned. Harold had brought
camping equipment. As night came on we were near the
center of South Dakota. Just as it was getting quite dark
Harold drove a little off the highway into a field. We set
up our army cots, one on each side of the car.

There was not a sound. The stars were high above us.
There is a peaceful feeling in such a location, far from
the sounds and lights of even a village, a peace that city
dwellers may never experience. Harold had loved our beautiful farm even though he didn't want to be a farmer.
Have you ever slept out under the stars? It is an unfor-
getable experience. On very warm nights in Phillipsburg
my mother and I sometimes slept out on our platform
porch on army cots.

106

Harold and I woke when the sun came up. We were in a wheat field, but the army worms had been there before us. The slim little worms appear in such hordes they are like an army. Those army worms had harvested the wheat. The ground was bare. There was nothing left save the soil of the field, and here and there a small piece of wheat stem. Silence everywhere.

HOME, peace, safety, love—a few weeks as it were out of the world of struggle. The faith of my family in me an assured thing—no competition, no judgment—only acceptance, consideration and confidence in me.

My friend from Imperial came for a few days, then took me back with him to visit friends and see again his big ranch on the South Divide and his herd of white faces in the canyons.

CHAPTER 10

A DIFFERENT MIND SET

THE PRESIDENT of the college at Aberdeen, that spring of 1931, wanted to help me so he made an appointment for me to see Dr. Lee Travis who was then the director of the speech pathology work at the University of Iowa.

"The tests show you should be left-handed. You are also strongly left-eyed." As Dr. Travis gave me that report of the series of tests he had put me through his voice was crisp and professional. He was then one of three or four outstanding specialists in a new field, speech pathology. Those handedness tests were all Dr. Travis seemed concerned with. Perhaps he thought there was no hope for me!

On that trip to Iowa City I bought myself a simple but most attractive silk dress with jacket. It was off-white or cream color. That dress was something of an extravagance since I was not to continue teaching at Aberdeen. In my rather lonely childhood it seems I had learned not to let myself be discouraged or depressed. I knew even then that one needs to be happy and to appear well. My mother wanted me always to be well-dressed. There must be a way to solve or at least alleviate any problem. One must keep cheerful as one seeks a happy outcome, but at that time I did not understand at all fully why I bought the dress.

The autumn of 1931 I returned to the University of Nebraska to work toward a Master's Degree in English Literature. My many happy associations with the university made me glad to be back there. Just to be on the campus was a joy. All my energies went into the discoveries accompanying the advanced study of literature. I knew a number of the professors. I was familiar with the buildings. Old University Hall, the first building of the university, had its own special atmosphere. The top floor had been condemned and removed, the first and second floors remained—everything about them old, the paint faded, the chairs carved, the floors worn and squeaky in some spots. The atmosphere of Old University Hall was of a decidedly earlier time, but some professors loved the old building and its atmosphere.

I deliberately assauaged my anxiety about my speech by turning to study—the study of literature, but I was not aware then that I was using an escape mechanism. It is only while writing this account, fifty years later, that I realize the psychological processes that were then operative.

Early in the winter of 1931-32 I consulted the head of the Speech Department at Nebraska, and after some months she found out the names of important speech pathologists who might help a stutterer. Robert West, Ph.D., at the University of Wisconson; Bryng Bryngelson, Ph.D., at the University of Minnesota; and Smiley Blanton, M.D., in New York City. I wrote to all three of them. I already knew of Lee Travis, Ph.D., at Iowa. Dr. Blanton was having a six-week summer school for speech cases at Williamstown, Massachusetts. Since I was a teacher he offered me a special rate, so I decided to go there.

I had shown myself capable of dealing with a serious problem at the time of the declamatory contest when I was eighteen. Then at the age of thirty I was faced with a complete block for my professional life unless or until I could get help for my stuttering. However I went to Dr. Blanton's summer school full of anticipation and prepared to enjoy those six weeks to the fullest. It would seem my daydreams—my escape from reality—assuaged my anxiety and fear.

A big fraternity house in a beautiful section of Williamstown was leased for the Speech Summer School. The wide lawn stretched down past red maples to a stream beyond which was a ridge of hills suggestive of mountains. Those hills challenged me to climb them. Mornings a mysterious haze hung over the valley and mounted up toward the summit of the hills. I had not seen so attractive a residence combined with so fine a view. Such a contrast between the beloved prairies where I grew up and that lovely Massachusetts scenery. Even the air was different.

There was a ratio of one staff member for four or five students. The pupils were of all ages, many from advantaged environments. I had not known people from such wealthy and privileged homes. Careful plans had been laid to make a happy, profitable summer for students and staff alike.

Mrs. Blanton, who knew color and make-up, gave some of us help as to which colors and textures were most becoming for us individually, along with make-up advice. Before that I had used rouge on my cheeks. Mrs. Blanton suggested lip stick, so from that time on I used lip make-up instead of rouge.

Dr. Blanton gave some rather informal lectures and discussions on Mental Health. He explained relaxation and something of its significance. Before that I had no concept of what relaxation really means. A small group of us were given physical education exercises in a way that stressed relaxation. Some evenings we had dancing lessons and then an hour of social dancing.

Dr. and Mrs. Blanton and their staff were splendid examples of relaxed persons. This started me thinking in terms of keeping myself relaxed. Relaxation is in part a state of mind, a mental outlook, a philosophy. But Dr. Blanton's aim was something more like peace of mind associated with physical relaxation. As I look back to that summer in that protected environment, I can in part recapture some of the atmosphere of peace, beauty and understanding of those six weeks. Dr. and Mrs. Blanton and their staff did the things that were conducive to relaxation, they maintained states of mind that helped them to relax, and they engaged in activities that lead to a calm, relaxing spirit. Dr. Blanton looked to golf for pleasure, exercise and a change from his daily work. That was certainly conducive to relaxation.

It is amazing how sometimes one makes the very best possible choice. That summer of study with Dr. Blanton opened up a new world for me. I gained considerable insight into my own complexes and the effect those complexes were having on my behavior. My horizons were broadening. I was a little nearer to becoming the master of my own fate. To become the true master of my own fate I had to accept responsibility for all phases of my life.

"Muscle-tensions" and their relation to relaxation were explained. The term muscle-tension is somewhat self-explanatory. To quote from Dr. Blanton's *Child Guidance,* 1927, p. 26:

> Of equal value with the conditioned response in the education of the child is this capacity to learn from the muscle-tensions of an individual his attitude toward a given object. This capacity is shown very early in infancy, and indeed, seems to account for much behavior which is usually thought of as "inherited." That is especially true with regard to fears and to likes and dislikes exhibited at an early age.

Muscle-tensions were mentioned at the end of Chapter One in the account of my crying. My parents said I cried an abnormal amount of the time from my birth until I was nine months old.

Dr. Blanton had a vast field of knowledge, experience and insight. After working in child guidance, he organized the speech pathology work at the University of Wisconsin, and also did some work at the University of Minnesota. Then he studied to become a psychiatrist. Shortly afterward he went to Vienna and was psychoanalyzed by Dr. Sigmund Freud. Then Dr. Blanton became a psychoanalyst himself.

Perhaps I thought there was going to be some magic by which Dr. Blanton could help my speech. I was surprised to learn he was a psychoanalyst. I knew nothing of psychoanalysis, but I had heard some negative views of it. I thought the matter over and concluded I would try in every way to profit by the summer.

I had some difficulty giving free associations, but I had a few dreams to take to my meetings with Dr. Blanton. One dream was composed of a number of symbols. Dr. Blanton said such a dream could be analyzed by the psychoanalyst. The symbols of that dream revealed a strong erotic attachment to my father. That was somewhat shocking after my puritanical upbringing. Now, fifty years later, I realize the dream interpretation was correct, and, moreover, that it should not be at all shocking to anyone. The strange thing about the analysis of this dream is that since that time I no longer remember my dreams. It was as though I no longer dreamed. Even now I can seldom remember even a fragment of a dream.

I am of a personality that I must try to figure things out for myself. Finally Dr. Blanton realized I needed to do some reading on psychoanalysis so he loaned me some books. I needed a subject for a Master's Thesis in English Literature. Dr. Blanton suggested the relationship of the poetess Elizabeth Barrett to her father.

My speech was not much different after those six weeks at Dr. Blanton's summer school, but I was beginning to get a broader view of life, and some insight into the working of the mind. I gained some vision of what Dr. Blanton's work represented. The aim was for a broader, deeper understanding and interpretation of what is important in life. I began to perceive different ways of looking at life and its problems. It seems to me now that I was beginning to get a mind-set so that I would go on and find a way to change my speech.

114

THE DUST BOWL years of the midwest were a time of depression all over the United States. During 1932 I was to teach in a small high school not far from my parent's home in Kansas. That winter I studied and took notes on the poetry of Elizabeth Barrett Browning and notes on the letters of Elizabeth Barrett and Robert Browning.

Every weekend I was home with my parents. For that reason I cherish the memory of that winter. It was a mild winter so the roads were not a problem. At that time in western Kansas good roads just had gravel on them, not the hard surfacing of today. That was the one winter since my rural-teaching years when I could be with my family other than Christmas and part of the summer. The warmth and love of home was strengthening for me, but even then I needed a life with less constricting boundaries and far wider horizons.

The American Speech and Hearing Association (ASHA) had recently been organized. The annual meeting for 1932 was at Thanksgiving time in St. Louis. I decided to attend and so learn a little more about therapy for stuttering. There I saw the leaders in what was then a new field. I saw and heard some stutterers there, stutterers who had worked to change their speech into a more acceptable form. Adults may not be able to eliminate the stuttering symptoms, but they can work to change them to a more acceptable form of speech.

THE WINTER of 1933-34 I was back at the University of Nebraska. I did quite a good thesis on "Recurrent Themes in the Writing of Elizabeth Barrett Browning." I was really interested in the deep attachment of a daughter to a dominating father. Mr. Barrett was determined to keep

Elizabeth dependent on himself even though that meant keeping her an invalid.

My advisor was Dr. White, an older professor, a scholar and a gentleman. He of course knew I was a stutterer. That was obvious! As the time drew near for my final examination for the Master's Degree, Dr. White counseled me to request a written examination in addition to the oral. I knew the professors who gave me the oral examination. It was a time of stress, but as I think back I even enjoyed that hour a bit. Of course I stuttered some in answering their questions. I received my Master's Degree in June, 1934.

IT WAS in 1932 I went east for work with Dr. Blanton. He let me go back and help at his school the summers of 1933 and 1934. Dr. Blanton was a person of deep insight. Through being at his school those three summers I gradually gained some in-depth understanding of myself and perhaps some vision of the possibilities life might hold for me. I began to gain some insight as to how to help myself. Certainly I was more relaxed than before I had worked with Dr. Blanton.

The winter of 1934-35 I was back at the University of Nebraska. I registered for two psychology courses and a beginning German course, preparatory to meeting the language requirements for the Ph.D. Degree. When the professor called on me to recite in German my stuttering was at its very worst. It was not until a year later that I was to find a way to face a professor or anyone in the wide world and use an acceptable speech pattern to say what I needed to express.

That winter I read English papers for a very wise,

116

kindly older professor, Dr. Stuff. The thought of going into speech pathology came to me slowly, and developed in my mind still more slowly. I talked to Dr. Stuff some about the advisability of transferring to speech pathology. As I think back, association with Dr. Stuff helped me a good deal. He had a daughter of his own who was a little older than I was. I was fortunate in the persons with whom I chose to talk over the matter, in that they helped me to consider the matter from all angles. No one encouraged me to go into speech pathology, on the other hand no one discouraged me.

So for three years I turned over and over in my mind the possibility, the advisability of going into speech pathology work. *There must be help for my speech; it was up to me to find such help.* As I think back it seems to me *there developed in me a quiet resolve, a fixed determination, to do whatever had to be done to improve my speech.* I came to have a very definite feeling that if I saturated myself with the literature on stuttering, that someway I would find help.

''THE SORROW of my predicament.'' I am convinced there is great significance in the words that at times come to one's mind as one meditates on a situation, a condition. It is now Thanksgiving time, a few years since I began writing this story. What a perfect opportunity I had in 1932 to talk out my psychological problems with a particularly kind and understanding person of wide experience and great wisdom—Dr. Smiley Blanton. I was so deep in my complexes I could not do free associations. The analysis of my very significant dream blocked my remembering any more dreams. It was truly "The sorrow of my predicament."

Possibly it would have been a help had I started making notes, and organizing them through the years that followed. My writing during these past few years has been the greatest possible blessing for me. I began my story to help other stutterers, but no one could be a greater recipient of benefits that those coming to me during this writing, the making of notes and then reorganizing them into a whole, somewhat a reconstruction of my life experiences.

THERE WAS some uncertainty, that winter of 1934-35, but I was not depressed. I was going on very little money. Kansas farm people go on toiling even though the rains fail to come. I was very busy with the college courses and with reading papers. I was thirty-three years old. A bright light gleamed for the future if I could just get my speech under some control. The past three years, with even a very limited study of psychoanalysis, had extended my view as to some of the possibilities for life—possibilities I had little clue to before my study with Dr. Blanton, but little did I dream what a broadening of interests and insights the future might still hold for me.

It finally seemed to me I hadn't many options. I felt I could not in honesty apply for a teaching position with my stuttering as it was, so the future might not be so bright as the past. Had my family lived in a city where there were factories, it might have seemed in my earlier years that I should turn to factory work. I had never been expected to do much work on the farm. All I knew was to do well with books in school and to be a conscientious teacher.

It was my speech problem, my future. I, I alone, had to accept responsibility for the outcome of my problem. The pattern for my life was about to be shaped by my stuttering—but I changed that. This was of the greatest importance for me, and it is of the very greatest importance in the rehabilitation of any stutterer. I cannot stress this too much. Once I reached a decision I held to that plan. There was no weakening in my resolve after I finally thought matters through to a conclusion. It seems there were no negative feelings, no resistance. The only consideration was to come to a wise decision, to attempt what could really help me.

There are times when one stands alone even with ones nearest and dearest all about one. Thus, in reality, I stood all alone with my family beside me, but it was I who had to make the final choice, the real decision. It was my future, my stuttering. It was I who must someway repay a loan if I borrowed money. Most of all it was the rest of my life before me—my destiny that had to be played out. Could I have had any concept of what a future with dependable speech might hold for me there would have been not even an instant hesitation. The University of Iowa seemed foremost in research on stuttering, so I began making plans to go there.

I did not go to Iowa to see if someone there could help me. I went to get help. It was up to me to someway get help there, help myself or find someone there who could point a way to help.

119

CHAPTER 11

IOWA

I OBTAINED a small educational loan from the PEO
organization through the help of a public-spirited
woman in our home town. I owe her a debt of gratitude.
As I look back I rather marvel at my courage. My parents
never fully realized the degree of my speech problem
because I stuttered so slightly in the easy speech situations
at home. They could not help me financially, but they
did not try to talk me out of what I was planning to do.

Had there been a different option that autumn of
1935 before I went to Iowa, I would have been sorely
tempted to choose that. I realize that clearly now. Then
was the time I had fears, doubts and uncertainties, but
these uncertainties seem not to have affected me very
deeply. I did not feel much different than times when I
had a teaching position to fill. It seems my daydreams
were a factor in easing my tensions and anxieties, and
then there was the security of the parental home.

In August my bachelor friend from Imperial, Nebraska,
came to see me. During those mild early autumn days
we drove on many side roads around Phillipsburg. The
roadside grass was full of early autumn sounds. Either

these were different bugs and insects, or the same insects of mid-summer made different sounds as autumn came on. It was a few weeks before frost, but the areas of native grasses were showing rainbow colors that an artist might only dream to take the place of the greens of spring and of midsummer. It would be weeks before the cottonwoods would turn to pure gold. There was a change in the odors as well as the sounds. The scents of autumn were already in the air, some spicy, some herbal.

When my friend took me to visit at Imperial, we always drove out to see his fields on the South Divide and his big herd of cattle, every one with a white face. (On my walk today I note the pampas grass is at its best now—great clumps of it in the next canyon to the west, huge clumps in all the canyons, the day so calm the great silky white plumes scarcely move. Some clumps seem high as my big orange tree.) My friend's pasture was on sandhill and canyon land, just at the edge of the Divide. Some of those canyons at certain times of the day or evening seemed enveloped in mystery. I could have come to love them.

Yet even then in 1935 I could not have been content to spend the rest of my life far from the city with its cultural and educational advantages. The feel of the city was in my blood, but it was more than that. I had a great need to know, to understand, to experience more than life had yet shown me. Nor could my friend have lived away from his ranch. We both realized how life had separated us.

We discussed my going to Iowa, and some about my stutter. He must have known my going would take us further than ever from each other. His thinking, as a large-scale rancher and as a pillar of his community, was figured

122

by the thousands. Four thousand bushels of corn, ten thousand bushels of wheat, a hundred fifty prime steers fattening to "top the market" at the very best time of the winter. He could not fully understand me, yet he sincerely wished me well as he kissed my cheek.

His presence is near me as I sit typing this story in my San Diego home. (The two Perfume Delight roses I cut this morning fill the room with their radiance.) I wish he were living and could come visit me now. We would have much talking to do for he was a quiet person, but with deep feeling. He was older than I but we would still be fond of each other. Nay, were he living it would be better for us to meet in the mid-west we both loved then, and to see and hear again life as we experienced it fifty years ago.

Before I was fully established in my work in Racine, his brother telephoned early one school morning. Death had come unexpectedly. For some moments I stood looking far, far out on Lake Michigan. The water was pale blue. Gulls were soaring over the shore. Then it was necessary for me to hasten my preparations for that school day. Again my eyes were far, far out on the water...a gentle, caring voice...golden fields of wheat and every animal in the herd with a white face... the canyons were more mysterious as evening came on. I heard that tender, affectionate voice as I would hear it so many times in memory in future years. The Lake was then a silvery, hopeful blue.

AT THE UNIVERSITY of Iowa I registered for psychology and speech pathology courses. I could not quite separate myself completely from the past, so I took a two-hour course in literature.

In his Speech Pathology course Dr. Lee Travis pointed
out that all speakers have speech deviations; the stutterer
just has more deviations in kind and severity. For a few
weeks I wrote down the speech deviations of Dr. Travis
and the other professors with whom I had classes. There
were only minor deviations of course, but I was taking
action. I was not just accepting statements about
stuttering.

Dr. Travis advised stutterers to observe their own stuttering pattern in a mirror—to do this for a half-hour or
so each day. On the basis of the way the stutterer automatically moved his mouth, tongue and jaw muscles during
stuttering, he might find an "easier," less tense way of
stuttering. Also the stutterer was advised to try imitating
his stutter—that is, to "fake" stuttering blocks. Sometimes stutterers were sent out to fake stuttering before
their friends, before students at the university, before
people in the city, on the streets. Faking was not to avoid
stuttering, but to advertise it. Also the faking should be
done, if at all possible, *before* a stutter comes, *even before
stuttering is anticipated.* In a slightly different sense *faking
was to imitate stuttering movements but to keep the
movements completely under voluntary control.*

This was a beginning for taking an aggressive stance
toward stuttering.

By following this advice from Dr. Travis, Wendell Johnson, while a young student with a very severe stutter, had
arrived at what was termed "The Bounce." All the years
I knew Dr. Wendell Johnson he used the bounce pattern
in all his speaking. For instance, the bounce goes something like this: "Whe-whe-whe-when I spea-spea-speak I
use the bou-bou-bounce like this." It served Dr. Johnson

well and his stuttering became less and less obvious as the years went by. He lectured in Racine a year or so before his fatal heart attack.

Dr. Travis still believes his advice to stutterers in the 1930s was correct. In a letter dated May 4, 1985, Dr. Travis from his home in Encino, California, states: "Yes, I would recommend the favorable support of faking stuttering even before it occurs, as a therapeutic procedure in the management of stuttering." This is now more than fifty years after I was in his speech pathology class.

Dr. Wendell Johnson had some late afternoon meetings for anyone interested in stuttering. Some university students like myself attended these meetings, some who were at Iowa City just for the Speech Clinic, and some normal-speaking students came to learn more about stuttering.

In one of these meetings someone used a few prolongations on vowel sounds—as one method of faking stuttering. Immediately I asked Dr. Johnson if one could fake stuttering that way. His reply was, "Oh, yes." So I began trying to prolong vowel sounds—as a start in working on my stuttering. It was something concrete I could try out and experiment with. In reality that started me on the pattern I was to use for the remainder of my life—a pattern to aid in more satisfactory management of my incidents of stuttering. So let me explain how a stutterer can effortlessly prolong sounds. One way is for the stutterer to prolong vowels in various words the stutterer can say without blocking. All vowel sounds can be prolonged. This is not a repetition of the sound, as a-a-a-a, nor is it using *ah* or *uh* before a sentence, or between phrases. *A prolongation should be held at a constant pitch.* It is not a slur or a glide. It is an effortless drawing out or prolonging of the exact vowel as it is in the word. Great care should be taken that the prolongation is on the exact vowel sound. All continuant sounds—F and V, S and Z, both the whispered and the voiced TH sounds, WH and W, SH and the voiced equivalent of SH as in pleasure can be prolonged; also the nasal sounds M, N, NG. It seems the continuant sounds should be easy to prolong, but I never found them nearly as satisfactory to prolong as the common vowels. The most frequently used vowel sounds are the ones on which I found it easiest to use prolongations. The *a as in father* and the *u as in up* seem the easiest, the simplest vowel sounds for me. For the *a as in father* one just opens one's mouth a little and lets the sound come out. For the *u as in up* one simply opens one's mouth a little wider. For the other vowel sounds, it seems to me, there is slightly more tension in the position.

Dr. Travis and Dr. Johnson both urged all us stutterers to write out early biographical incidents in our lives. I tried but I couldn't write anything that seemed in any way significant for me or for my stuttering. Now, in my retirement, it took months for me to think through to the incidents in the first chapters of this story. But I do now feel Dr. Travis was right and that during a stutterer's stay in a speech clinic and also after he leaves the clinic it will be wise for him to write out every day a page or two of whatever associations come to his mind *whether or not they seem to relate to his speech.* He should date these pages and keep them.

I began trying to use prolongations of sounds in my talking. After I learned about prolonging sounds, for the first time I had an alternative to stuttering. I could choose: go ahead and stutter, or try to use prolongations. I tried prolonging sounds in very easy speech situations. I would begin my sentence with a word I probably would not stutter on, and I would prolong on the first vowel sound in that word. I should have read aloud every day in my room and prolonged on many sounds, but it did not occur to me to do that, besides I was quite busy with the courses I was taking. I made rather a slow start—I was taking my time about everything.

In successful faking there is no undue tension. I found that prolonging some sounds often enabled me to relax somewhat. I think it was the fact that the prolonging of vowel sounds in a way put me at ease and enabled me to relax, that encouraged me to go on with the prolonging of sounds. This is an extremely significant point. I distinctly recapture that feeling of fifty years ago. I had learned enough about relaxation to be conscious of some of its advantages, and that in the main, normal-speaking persons were for the most part calm and relaxed.

During stuttering there is tension, sometimes enormous tension, and at times thought disintegration. The entire body is involved in the stuttering act. When an individual is entrapped in a stuttering incident the all-important need is to get the sound out—to get the word said. A stutterer feels complete and utter humiliation when he stutters severely and helplessly. Even a slight stuttering block humbles and embarrasses a stutterer. In successful prolonging of sounds or using a voluntary speech pattern I find that urgency gone. If the urgency is there the stutterer may not have achieved a voluntary, effortless prolongation. *Any plan for the management of the stuttering symptom should include some way to relieve the tension and stress accompanying stuttering.* I feel assured

127

the relaxation work I had with Dr. Blanton in 1932 was a real help at Iowa in 1935-36. The psychoanalytical insight I gained in my work with Dr. Blanton and through independent reading of Freud's books enabled me to understand, to comprehend on a level I could not have otherwise, and also helped relieve the very deep and basic emotional conflicts in my life.

At that time the University of Iowa was the center that was doing the most thorough investigations into stuttering. Several young men-stutterers, that autumn of 1935, had casts put on their right arms so they were forced to use their left hands. These were persons that tests had shown should be left-handed. After six weeks the casts were removed, but put back on after a very few weeks. This approach was finally given up as not practical for young-adult and adult stutterers. The recommendation was made that care should be taken that young children be free to use their left hands, that is to choose their own handedness. Dr. Blanton had investigated change of handedness for stuttereres, but found it impractical.

In 1931 Dr. Travis concluded I should have been left-handed. Twenty years later while I was teaching speech therapy in Racine, Wisconsin, I did a little experimenting and found I readily learned a fairly new activity for my left hand. For many years I bought whole coffee beans and ground some each morning for my coffee. I found I quickly became accustomed to turning my coffee grinder with my left hand, and I could turn a hand eggbeater with my left hand as easily as with my right. I experimented a very little with trying to write with my left hand, and to eat with my left hand, but I never seriously tried to change handedness. The improvement in my

128

speech came without any change in my handedness, but as I write this in 1984 the basic stuttering is still in me— much as it was during my teenage years. Possibly had I been left-handed from my earliest years there would have been no stuttering. My present good speech is dependent on my prolonging a few sounds when I talk—practically every time I speak before anyone, and on my keeping a very objective attitude about my stuttering. Even when I read aloud at home alone I need to prolong a few sounds. Since I have been writing this story, I speak freely of my stuttering to people around me, so that now my stuttering is almost an attraction, a benefit, a subject of interest for people I meet and talk with.

A few days ago an incident occurred which fills me with awe, and causes me to rethink the matter that in 1931 Dr. Travis found I should have been left handed. My neighbor needs to learn lip reading, to become expert with it. I feel that familiarity with some of the groupings of sounds I learned in phonetics and that I used with my pupils while I taught in Racine, Wisconsin, should be helpful for her. Thus, with a black marking-pencil I made some small charts for her. One chart was the six plosive sounds, the whispered on the left, the voiced on the right.

P	B
T	D
K	G

The letter D did not look correct to me. I traced over it, but still it did not look right. The next day when I went to my neighbor's with my charts, just as I reached her home, I realized what was amiss with my letter D. I had reversed it, that is, the curved part was on the left instead of the right.

AT ONE TIME, while I was in college or teaching, I had difficulty with the capital N. I discovered I was making it upside down. I still need to think when I print a capital letter N, also I must pause to think when there is an occasion to write a capital letter E. A reversed written capital letter E would be the number 3. All of this seems to be evidence of a basic confusion in my neurological system. My mother taught me at home for two years. I have no memory of reversals in my printing of letters or numbers, but if or when there were I am certain she carefully, most patiently and lovingly, showed her beloved little girl over and over the correct way. I do have a fleeting memory of asking which way the curved part of a letter or a number went.

The hope for teenage and adult stutterers is that the stuttering symptoms may be modified, changed so that the stutterer does not suffer a professional handicap, and that the stutterer's basic tension and anxiety be relieved. The important thing is not the number of stuttering incidents, but the way they are managed. As Dr. Charles Van Riper has written, "...we can learn to accept stuttering as a problem and be willing to work to change it to a form less abnormal..."

If a stutterer achieves better speech through methods that do not relieve his tension and anxiety, that individual may later be a victim of high blood pressure or even a heart attack. My total study, experience and observation of stuttering and stutterers leads me to this conviction. Stutterers are inclined to feel "relieve my stutter and my tension and anxiety will vanish,'' but this is not necessarily the result. I cannot over-emphasize the point that whatever methods are used to relieve the stuttering, those procedures should relieve the tension and anxiety. Sometimes training in relaxation can help. The matter of strain and tension can be most difficult to deal with. Psychoanalysis should help, or play therapy for small children. People may be extremely intelligent and capable but have no concept of what deep relaxation really means.

There were many stutterers in Iowa City, some had found work there. A type of group therapy for stutterers certainly was operative. Stutterers were urged to use faked-stuttering, to hunt out all manner of situation in which to talk before many different people in all stations of life. The people of Iowa City responded and would in common courtesy listen to a stutterer—listen patiently whether it was real or faked stuttering. No such situation existed anywhere else—in the world. Everyone was interested in stuttering, stutterers and non-stutterers alike. So Iowa City was an ideal place for anyone to work on his stuttering. It was a sheltered workshop. The real survive-or-perish test for me was to come in 1938 when I went to teach at Racine, Wisconsin. This sheltered environment at Iowa made it easier to start to work on one's stuttering, but the stutterer has to live in the world. From such a sheltered environment he must be prepared to carry on out in the world of reality with anything he has been doing to modify his stuttering.

Clinicians who wish to work with stutterers should do weeks of talking with some kind of faking pattern. In the 1960 best-selling novel ''To Kill a Mockingbird'' Harper Lee says: ''You never really understand a person until you consider things from his point of view...until you climb into his skin and walk around in it." (p. 36)

I talked to many stutterers and learned something of what different ones were doing for their speech. How did I personally feel toward those persons who stutter? I felt sympathy. I was one of them. I think I would not have chosen one of them for a close friend, or to be seen much with in public. Their stuttering somewhat embarrassed me, so if I, a stutterer, felt embarrassed by the speech of other stutterers, normal speakers must feel embarrassed by my stuttering! This may have been a spur to keep me trying, trying to fit into something that would enable me to get help.

I realized that some stutterers had modified, changed their stuttering sufficiently that they could advance professionally—even with modified stuttering, so it was up to me to effect some change in my own stuttering pattern in order that I too might hope to advance professionally. A more realistic hope for the future began to glimmer in the distance. It was a great game with enormously high stakes for me that I was playing, but I though little of that. I was just going along doing what I saw to do. I never felt the work I did on my speech to be a punishment.

My therapy was largely self-directed, but please remember I was surrounded by the very best advice, that is by the lectures of Dr. Lee Travis and Dr. Wendell Johnson, and I had studied with Dr. Smiley Blanton. Thus I could choose only from the best advice. I believe those specialists gave the very best counsel available for stutterers then or now. I was not aware that there might be any other way to attack the stuttering symptom than by faking stuttering, and by doing the faking well before a stutter came. It

132

seems some stutterers used what they termed "good mental hygiene." I learned a good deal about mental hygiene
at Dr. Blanton's summer school, all of which was excellent
for me personally, but the mental hygiene principles did
not in any way relieve my stuttering symptoms. On the
other hand I feel assured the work with Dr. Blanton
enabled me to enter more fully into the faking of stuttering
and all the work on the stuttering symptom. The attitude
of the stutterer is the crucial link and there was endless
resolve and determination in me.

I think I tried out every suggestion that was made by
the professors at Iowa. I felt I could take my time about
it, but before long I must do some organized work to help
my stuttering, and I probably should do it under someone's
supervision and direction if I were to get the maximum
benefit. I had gone to Iowa to get help for my stuttering.
I was gradually accepting responsibility for my own speech,
and thus for the outcome of my work at Iowa. This was
of the utmost importance. One does not make haste in
working on stuttering. Perhaps one must feel one's way—
edge along a cliff with the best light one can get for
guidance.

I was having some difficulty learning to write up
psychology experiments. I could write literary things for
English classes, but psychology experiments, I was finding,
were to be written in quite a different style.

I had grown up a protected child and young person.
Often I needed someone's approval to help me to a decision. I didn't realize it then, but such dependence divided or shifted the responsibility for the outcome. It was
well that I take the responsibility for the method I used
in working on my stuttering. At the time of the declam-

atory contest I practiced voice exercises that gave me a slightly different way of speaking. But with my prolongations of sound I was using my normal conversational voice, only I was drawing out certain sounds, chiefly vowel sounds.

The routine way was for a stutterer to be assigned a speech clinician who would have conferences with the stutterer and attempt to lay out a scheme of assignments and exercises that would be of the greatest possible benefit for that individual stutterer. I hesitated to ask for a speech clinician, for I knew myself well enough to realize it would have to be just the right person if I were to receive real help. If I took steps to get a clinician and then if I could not work with that individual, I would be in real trouble. So in a way I was marking time, but I was using some prolongations in my talking.

CHAPTER 12

200 SPEECH SITUATIONS

I HAD HEARD Dr. Charles Van Riper's name barely mentioned a time or two. He worked with some of the men stutterers. One noon near the end of my first semester at Iowa, I was going along the hall in the basement of the psychology department building. That structure had its own atmosphere. The boards of the floor were worn. All the students, all the professors with their dreams and doubts who had lingered, hurried along those halls. I was tired but I did not need to hurry just then.

I came upon a tall, pipe-smoking young man who was fixing some equipment for an experiment. We talked a bit. He was stuttering a good deal, but in a controlled sort of way. It gradually dawned upon me who this was.

"You are Dr. Van Riper?"

We talked a few mintutes more and as we talked I felt, "This person could help me." I thought fast and said "I'm going to have to get myself a speech clinician." Surely there was pleading in my voice—please help me!

In the blinking of an eyelid Dr. Van Riper responded, "I'll give you an assignment."

I still hear his voice saying those words. I was surprised, nonplused at his quick response. Gently I asked, "What would the assignment be?"

"Go out and stutter before 200 people and bring me their names."

We discussed the matter a little. I could write down that I asked directions of two men students at the corner of Oak and Center, or that I stuttered before three students in a psychology class, but the 200 persons had to be rather specific. I did not make any statement that I would accept the assignment and do it, but it was absolutely clear in my own mind that I would do it. I still recall the very first speech situation I did for Dr. Van Riper's list. I stopped two young men students to ask directions. I prolonged some sounds and stuttered on some. They were too polite to show irritation. I wanted to laugh and say I was doing speech situations. A bitterly cold wind was blowing. I thought, "No, I should not admit faking, I should keep that as a situation in which I really needed help with directions." I do not recall that anyone else was using prolongations as I used them, but that did not make any difference to me if the prolonging of vowel sounds could really help me.

When a person is in the act of stuttering there is a distortion of the sound that an observer hears, and there is often a good deal of tension that an observer sees. During stuttering, tension can be seen on the face, often great facial distortion. I recall one young woman—when she began to stutter, her hand would begin going up to hide her mouth. Sometimes the entire body of the stutterer

136

is tense. Viewed objectively, a stutterer looks and sounds ludicrous, sometimes as though he is being tortured. In reality he is experiencing some degree of mental anguish. If one can do faking of stuttering that is completely voluntary, with no element of stuttering, the urgency is gone, also the devastating effect, and the agony. When the stutterer has achieved a relaxed prolongation he is in full control of his speech processes. Any work or any treatment to aid a stutterer should be planned so it may act to relieve the stress and tension associated with the stuttering. I cannot emphasize this too much. Too many stutterers develop a heart condition in mid-life.

At the time I was practicing for the declamatory contest I was using a different voice for my declamation. I also did exercises to increase the volume of my voice. When I gave my salutatorian speech I was using my natural tone of voice and I did stutter a bit.

I have known of two professors with stutters who did not stutter while teaching their classes. Perhaps they used what I term "a different tone of voice" for their classroom lectures. But in prolonging sounds I was using my natural speaking tone of voice. It was the prolonging of vowel sounds, plus a feeling of relaxation, that enabled me to use the prolongations successfully, and to make that a bridge to normal speech.

In his excellent book *A Stutterer's Story* Dr. Frederick P. Murray tells of a time he played the part of Neptune when the ship he was on, going to Australia, crossed the equator. Fred Murray is a tall, rather distinguished-looking man, so it was natural the ship's social director should choose him, but she of course did not know he stuttered. By that time Fred Murray had had considerable help with his stutter and was teaching at the University of New Hampshire. He writes of "role changes." To quote from Dr. Murray's book, pp. 37–8.

There are many degrees and kinds of role changes that may affect a stutterer's fluency. A rather dramatic one occurred in 1972 when I was on a ship bound for Australia, about to cross the equator. The ship's social director had organized the presentation of a traditional ceremony. She asked me to play the part of the prosecutor in King Neptune's court. I was apprehensive because it meant having to read aloud from a long script, and I knew from other voyages that almost everyone on board would be listening, some hanging from the balconies of the upper decks, others sitting in rows on the main deck. However, I put on my costume of robes and hat and beard, and went off by myself to develop an appropriate voice for the part—one a little deeper than my own, more melodic, more deliberate and confident-sounding. I'm sure both the costume and the new voice contributed to my feeling, once I began to speak in the actual ceremony, that I really was the prosecutor. I found I was having a wonderful time, booming away in rolling rhythms, with no sign of stuttering at all.

THE PROLONGING of vowel sounds that I did was quite different from stuttering. There was no undue stress or tension in my face or in my voice, unless or until in what

138

I was saying, I experienced real stuttering. Any vowel sound can be prolonged or drawn out with relative ease, at least that is my experience. The word is distorted, but without tension. The extent of the distortion depends on the length of the prolongation. One can even enjoy the act of putting on a show and being in control. I speak of "prolonging sounds" in preference to the term "faking stuttering." Since stuttering breeds tension, faking stuttering might be associated with tension. Whereas prolonging sounds to me indicates a calm, relaxed normal sound that is just prolonged or drawn out a bit. Stuttering tends to bring on tension, and more tension; in contrast, prolonging sounds can lead into a happy, calm, relaxed state. Also the term "prolonging sounds" is an exact description of what I do.

I feel certain the relaxation training I had at Dr. Blanton's Speech Summer School helped me with the prolonging at Iowa. (The enchanting song of the white-crowned sparrows fills the air this morning. Now in October they are returning to southern California from their nesting in the arctic. The arctic may be either the arctic zone on a high mountain, or the area north of the Arctic Circle in Canada. It relieves the stress I still feel in discussing stuttering to think of something entirely different, thus the following series of digressions about the white-crowned sparrows in this chapter serve as safety valves for my feelings. In a way my mention of birds or flowers are daydreams darting in and out of my consciousness.) I tried to do the prolonging in a very relaxed way. For instance after I had used a half-dozen fake prolongations I felt more relaxed than before I began speaking. The very act of prolonging a sound in a relaxed way enabled me to keep or to attain some degree of relaxation. In other terms, I was doing an act I had made a considered decision to do. I was in control. I began carrying a piece of paper and a pencil at all times so I could write down each speech situation as I did it. It seems I felt absolute confidence that the doing of speech situations and the prolonging of sounds would help me. The advice to fake stuttering came from the best authority I knew. It was a carefully thought-out plan for the intelligent management of one's stuttering.

All stutterers, I believe, find they can sometimes sub-stitute an easy word for a word they would stutter on. Stutterers quite universally do this. I had become an expert at substituting words, possibly as early as third or fourth grade, soon after I entered school. Then at Iowa I felt I must give up this crutch if I were going to get my stuttering under some control. When I gave up substituting words of course I had many more stuttering blocks. Eventually I did mention to Dr. Van Riper that I should give up substituting words. He of course agreed with me that substituting words could have no place in working on my stuttering.

It was time to register for the second semester, so I was talking to more and to different people. I used pro-longations of vowel sounds in words and phrases I could say with no difficulty. I recall I made some of the pro-longations quite long, but I had stuttering too that I could not do anything about—then. "Whi---------ch way----i------s the mea------------t ma---rket?" The prolongations should be of varying lengths. Great care must be taken that such prolongations remain effortless and do not turn into stuttering, or that one does not just develop a different pattern of stuttering. (The white-crowned sparrows have more spirit than the birds which are resident here. There is a sprightliness in their movements that the house finches lack. They regularly eat seeds on my terrace, which is almost at ground level, but they will not put their heads inside a bird feeder to get seeds.) I would even take a breath sometimes in the middle of a prolongation, and then go on prolonging the sound. "I-------t is co---------(breath)---------ld today." Each prolongation for a beginner should be two or three seconds long. Four seconds can seem an eternity as one begins to work on this. May I suggest the reader, watch in hand, try some three and four second prolongations.

Dr. Tiffin, one of the psychology professors, said I was the most severe stutterer he had ever heard. In truth, I was the stutterer with the largest number of unusually long prolongations. Many of them were effortless—real fakes, but of course at that time I had real stuttering, too. I suspect Dr. Tiffin understood in part what I was doing.

I cannot be certain exactly when it was that I began another type of list. I wrote down all the words on which I stuttered. I should have written down every word on which I thought I would stutter, but I did not think of that then. This writing down of these words was an acknowledgement of my stuttering; as such it helped to make me objective. If I could not write down one of these words, I at least made a mark, and I explained to anyone near me what I was doing. A stutterer knows when he is stuttering, even when he is going to stutter. How does he identify a stutter? Perhaps it is no more than tension in his mouth. It seems to me the making of this list of

141

stuttered words was important. *It was in my thinking that is was important to clearly distinguish between stuttered words and normal speech.*

I did nothing with the words on that list, but I should have worked on them. I should have worked out ways of faking on them, and then made occasions in which I could use those words. In one light I was making of this a great adventure, but I had to succeed or I was a lost soul. It was a venture worth making come about. It was not only necessary to improve, but how I did it was of immense concern for me. I still recall something of my feeling as I was writing down those words I stuttered on. I did not feel bad about any of it. There was no hiding my speech deviations, no matter where I was or to whom I was talking. It was a bit like playing a game, or having a part in a drama. I was becoming very objective about my speech. It was no longer just my little speech problem, but here it was out for all the world to observe. At times I was even a bit amused over the situation.

Iowa provided an atmosphere in which I could develop a way I could help myself, a way for me to work on my own stuttering and to sort out procedures which enabled me to try ways to help myself.

It was a delight, as well as a relief, an incalculable reward for me to feel this change in my speech taking place. I was gradually gaining control in the management of my stuttering. It seemed little short of a miracle that was happening to me, but my feet were solidly on the ground. I had to make good grades in the courses I was taking. I was really very matter of fact about this work on my speech and the relief I was experiencing. No doubt the passing of the years has helped me to get events and influences in my speech improvement into perspective, so that I can now more clearly evaluate the various factors and influences. Prolonging vowel sounds helped to build up self-confidence in me. In talking I began prolonging on the first vowel sound, and I prolonged many vowels after that. *I did not wait until I had a stuttering block to begin prolonging some of my sounds.* I would choose wording to begin my sentence so that I could easily prolong a sound in the first word. After years of experimenting with my own stuttering and with doing speech therapy work, I feel this is a difference of real significance, that is, to begin and to continue faking *before* there is real stuttering.

I am certain that in part I worked out for myself how and when to fake stuttering. What I used was the prolonging of sounds, mostly vowel sounds. *I started the prolongations before I even felt stuttering.*

I realized I was just getting started, venturing forth with a speech pattern that set me apart from others. I did not think ahead of having to use this faking, this prolonging of sounds, every day, on every occasion for speaking, for the remainder of my life. Even if I had considered all that, it would be a small price for the satisfaction, the reward, the joy, the glory of knowing I could depend on being able to express myself. For the first time in my thirty-four years I could rely on being able to say what I wanted to.

It was an occasion for quiet rejoicing, that spring of 1936, that I was acquiring a pattern, a method through which I could express myself—express myself on any and all occasions. It would enable me to relate my thoughts, my feelings, even my dreams if I wished to. Furthermore

I could hold my head high with pride. The face of all the world was changing.

I was quite a busy person. I was carrying a full schedule of classes. I had changed from English Literature to psychology, so the subjects I was taking were not too easy for me. I had to budget my time, get the work on my stuttering in when I could. I was so very thankful I was getting help! But it was a quiet kind of rejoicing.

IOWA is the state where "the tall corn grows," often the very best corn on the top of the hills. It is a prosperous state with fine, big, old homes. Summers are hot and often humid, winters cold. In later years I drove through Iowa a number of times on the way between Kansas and Wisconsin.

Iowa City was then a college town of 25,000 population. The Iowa River divides the city. A few of my classes were on the other side of the river. It was a skin-chilling walk during mid-winter, but crossing the river was always interesting, and there were usually students going both directions.

The Jahnkes, an older couple, rented their upstairs rooms. There was a tiny make-shift kitchen. Mary C., not my high school chum, had one room. She sometimes wrote a poem, then she would read her poem to me. We carefully respected each other's time, but there were visiting moments every day. Sometimes we shared a baked potato. We are still close friends. Mary was working on her Ph.D. in English Literature. We both usually carried a paper-sack lunch. The Jahnkes were a hearty, friendly couple. We visited a bit most days. Jimmy, a five-year old grandchild, was with them. He had some problems learning to

144

talk so we all tried to help him. In a way for those two years we were one big family in that house. Of course I tried out my speech experiments on them. Mrs. Jahnke and I exchanged Christmas cards as long as she lived.

WELL, it must have taken me nearly two weeks to get a list of 100 persons before whom I had stuttered or faked stuttering. It was high time to do something in the way of a report to Dr. Van Riper. I went to him with my list. He was kind. He said it was very good, but he thought I ought to finish the assignment. That is, make him a complete list of 200 persons before whom I had stuttered or faked stuttering. In other words, I was to do another hundred. I felt I had to do this if Dr. Van Riper was going to be willing to try to help me. So I did it.

In a way I felt Dr. Van Riper was trying me out. Did I have enough concern to stay with a task and finish it. It was also making me more and more objective about my stuttering. This is of the very greatest importance, to be objective about one's problems. Get it out in the open and do things with it. (Several white-crowned sparrows are singing simultaneously, so their songs overlap. Their song has always said to me "Come li—ve with me—." In Wisconsin we saw and heard these birds only during their migrations, for two or three weeks, but for both spring and autumn migrations.)

As I think back, I realize that Dr. Van Riper saw I needed to be less sensitive and far more objective about my stuttering. Those 200 speech situations really turned the tide for me. To a large extent I could help myself after that. For the first time in my life I was becoming able to depend on my ability to express myself orally. I did not realize it then, or think much about it, but my prolonging of sounds was to become a way of life for me, an absolute survival technique.

There is another type of speech activity which I assuredly would have used had I though of it: To say one's thoughts and movements aloud. This can be done when one is alone. For instance while getting dressed, preparing and eating breakfast, walking along the street, even while driving a car. The stutterer needs to hear his own voice aloud—and to hear it in normal speech. So using faking, prolongations or whatever will enable him to speak fluently, the stutterer, when he is alone, could say his thoughts and movements aloud for a total of half an hour or more each day. Even if he can speak fluently without stuttering in such situations, he should do much faking and prolonging, one or two in each short sentence. For instance: "I thi-----nk I will get up a----nd get supper. I'll wa-------lk to the ki-----tchen. A baked po----tato would ta---ste good. I'll tur---n on the oven. I'll wash the po-----tato and cu---t off a bad spot or two. I'll also have squa------sh, I gue---ss."

It seems to me the stutterers who were registered students at the university received more benefit in the management of their stuttering than the ones who came just for work in the stutterer's clinic. It is a benefit for the stutterer to saturate himself with the literature of speech pathology. I feel even the study of phonetics was a personal benefit for my speech. It enabled me to understand more fully what I could do with sounds.

Within a few weeks after I met Dr. Van Riper and did the 200 speech situations I was doing quite well with my faking and prolonging of sounds. That is, until I came to

146

a plosive sound—P-B, T-D, K-G. I took the problem to Dr. Van Riper. Many of the exercises which help stutterers are very simple indeed, if the stutterer works at them faithfully.

Dr. Van Riper said. "One has a choice. The stutterer can either stop or go on when he feels stuttering."

Let me try to illustrate. For the word "pan" do not quite close the lips for the p sound. The resulting word is a distortion of "pan," but if the stutterer can be in control, that is the important thing. For "time" do not quite make a complete closure with the tongue against the upper gum ridge. Put the tongue so it almost touches back of the upper teeth. For "key" try to make a soft closure between the back of the tongue and the soft palate. The voiced equivalents of P, T, K (that is B, D, G) are made similarly with soft closures. When the stutterer practices alone with a mirror, he may be able to get the feel of normal speech and that glorious feeling of being in control of the sounds he produces. I never really mastered this way of dealing with plosive sounds. (A feeling of pure joy goes through me as I hear the white-crowned sparrows singing their rolicking song, and I begin to relax from the stress of just writing of stuttering. The winter of 1980, after the Mt. St. Helen's volcanic eruption, there were no white-crowned sparrows eating in my yard, and I rarely heard their song.) In the management of stuttering there are techniques or controls an individiual may learn to use that may seem to improve his speech, to lessen the degree of his stuttering, but such controls require effort, constant awareness. Any therapy, I am convinced, should relieve the tension of the stutterer. Perhaps that is the key test for the worth of any therapy for stuttering. Please

147

remember my prolongations are a simple drawing out of the vowel sounds. They are not slides or glides between consonants.

Dr. Frederick P. Murray, of the University of New Hampshire, in a letter dated June 10, 1985, states: "I, personally, am convinced that controls do sap one's energy and that one is rarely emotionally free when using them! However, they can serve a purpose, at times, when the only other alternative seems to be that of blocking a lot." Dr. Murray speaks with experience for he still has a remnant of the severe stuttering of his early years. Dr. Murray further elaborates: "To me stuttering often starts in other body parts and in states of mind, long before it affects the flow of oral speech." My own experience is that sometimes I feel the sensation of stuttering in my mouth when I have said nothing.

The therapies Dr. Smiley Blanton, Dr. Lee Travis and Dr. Wendell Johnson taught were all such as would promote relaxation in the management of stuttering.

Both Dr. Travis and Dr. Johnson urged stutterers to spend time each day observing their own stuttering in a mirror. Thus a stutterer may find an easier, less tense way of stuttering. In this way it is hoped a stutterer may find a way of helping himself. A clinician need not tell a stutterer how to change his stuttering, what pattern of stuttering or faking to use. It is my experience that the stutterer should try to work that out for himself—but with the best advice and counseling. Dr. Van Riper did not instruct me to use prolongations of sounds. He gave me the assignment to do 200 speech situations. It was up to me to work out how I did them. My use of prolongations of sounds in my talking was my adaptation of all I had learned about therapy for stuttering. This is completely clear to me now, fifty years later. *The wonderful thing about the prolonging of sounds that I learned to do the autumn of 1935 at the University of Iowa was that I felt freer, more relaxed, more in control, the moment I began to use the drawn-out sounds, even though every occasion when I used a prolongation required a distinct decision on my part.*

My use of prolongations of vowel sounds has never become automatic. When one is driving a car, using the brake pedal, or feeding gas with one's right foot becomes almost automatic. My using of prolonged sounds, even very slightly lengthened vowels, has never in any way become automatic or spontaneous. My prolonging of sounds is always a voluntary act. It is easy now in my retirement years to use prolongations, especially since I have been working, pondering for years over this book. Sometimes before people I know only casually I call attention to my lengthening of some sounds, and say a word of explanation as to why I am doing that. Each time I speak about my stuttering is a benefit. My resistance to using prolongations has decreased in most instances, but it is still a very real matter for me to constantly deal with.

YOU HAVE the story of my early life and of my family in some detail. What I have achieved was through perseverance. Remember the multiplication tables. From the account I have given you it would seem the work on my stuttering progressed with amazing ease, and in a way it did. On the other hand I am certain none of this was really as easy as it may seem in retrospect. Every normal speaking person who aspires to working with stutterers should put himself through at least six weeks of doing all the things with his speech that stutterers must do with theirs to attain anything like normal speech.

Since my high school days I had been a wanderer in a desert. Then at Iowa I could see clearly my future was in my own hands. It was my responsibility to make the work on my stuttering succeed. I was being shown a way. It was my responsibility to do whatever would help me, and to make certain I did not hold back. I surely would have been a poor weak thing if I could not have gone on.

You remember I was growing up before the First World War. Then there was no social security, no subsidy for farmers, no unemployment pay. One had to see to it that the necessities were someway provided. And you recall I felt my professional life was blocked unless or until I could get my stuttering under some control. I had borrowed money to go to Iowa. A loan must be repaid! I wanted to continue my professional life. I wanted to have a teaching career.

Circumstances in my life had formed me into a person who could do all this work on the stuttering symptom, but I also had some part that winter of 1935-36 in making myself simply go ahead doing all I knew to help my stuttering. Also I was most fortunate in having the guidance of such a person as Dr. Van Riper who had such keen insight into the problems of stutterers. He proved to be a "friend at court." Such a debt of gratitude I owe him for his insight and kindness in all his help! Even though there seemed to be some magic about it all, there was just plain work and keeping oneself courageous. What I have done any stutterer should be able to do. If you try

150

hard enough and can keep yourself from holding back, there may be, there will be some magic for you too. Sometimes, you know, magic is of our own making.

CHAPTER 13

A BREAK IN THE CLOUDS

IT HAS LONG been recognized that stuttering is cyclic, that is, in a child stuttering may come and go with no apparent reason, or be better or more severe. Speech pathologists who work with young adult stutterers are well aware of the danger of relapse within a few weeks, or even days, after the stutterer leaves the clinic. The summer of 1936 I was going to be home with my parents in Kansas. My speech was improving, and I was becoming quite objective about it. I had stopped substituting words, and I did some prolonging of sounds in every bit of conversation. I was determined I was going to keep the improvement I had made.

It seemed everyone around the psychology department at Iowa was doing experiments, so I thought I would do a bit of experimenting with my own stuttering. I bought Pavlov's book on the study of the conditioned response. I wanted the book to be mine so I could put marks in it. Pavlov showed food to a dog and rang a bell at the same time. The dog salivated. When the dog was conditioned, it salivated when the bell was rung even though no food was shown. Thus the dog manifested a conditioned reflex. It is an interesting book for a psychology student to read and reread.

When I arrived home I got out the book and explained to my parents that I wanted to read aloud to them every day because I needed an audience to read before. I think it may have bothered my mother some, to have made her a bit nervous, but my father entered wholeheartedly into my project. When he came home from work he would say "Well, let's get at the reading." At that time my father was working at a hardware store in Phillipsburg.

Summers in Kansas are warm, so around four in the afternoon we would turn on the hose, wash off the platform porch on the east side of our house, and water the spirea which grew in great clumps in front of the porch. (I well recall how lovely that spirea was in early spring—and fragrant. Some years the long rows of spirea on the Nebraska campus made a memory picture to recall the rest of one's life. At Nebraska one spring snow came while the spirea was at its best.)

After the porch was washed off it was quite pleasant there. We regularly sat out there at that time. It was peaceful, a time of quiet joy to be at home, especially with my speech improving and a possible happy professional future seeming to be opening for me. So after my father came home I would read aloud for a half-hour more or less, making many sounds long, all the time marking the words and sounds in which I used prolongations even though there was no stuttering. I used different colored marks for the words on which I felt stuttering and for the

154

words on which I faked stuttering but with no sensation of a stutter.

My thought in the oral reading was to keep my speech improving and to do something in the way of an experiment by determining which sounds I stuttered on, and the effect of daily oral reading and careful discrimination between words on which there was even a slight sensation of stuttering and words on which there was no sensation at all of stuttering. As I continued to work on this the determining factor came to be largely as to whether or not I felt tension in my mouth. *It seems my aim in using prolongations in my talking at that time was not only to eliminate the repetition and blocking of stuttering, but also to eliminate any sensation of stuttering on any word. As my speech improved during the summer, these discriminations became very fine points indeed.* An observer could not have discriminated as I did. From the oral reading, of course, I tried to carry these fine discriminations over into my conversational speech.

I did this practically every afternoon all during the summer vacation. Time after time I noted that the more prolongations I used and the longer I read, the fewer incidents of stuttering I felt. By the end of the summer there were too few words on which I felt the sensation of stuttering in my oral reading to do a study.

Perhaps I prolonged on a fifth, or even a fourth, of the words. Early in the summer possibly one in four prolongations was a fake. By the end of the summer that proportion was reversed, one in four prolongations I might identify as stuttering. There was no relapse. In addition my conversational speech was a bit better in the fall than when I first came home. Reading aloud is different from conversational speech. I cannot overemphasize the importance of that reading aloud and of constantly making judgments as to whether a prolonged sound was free of stuttering, or whether there was still an element of stuttering in it—and so should be marked with the color used for the stuttered words. I was slowly becoming the master of my own destiny. Note that I was making some aggressive moves in the management of my stuttering. It seems I was always thinking, questioning is this the best way?

Now in my mid-eighties it seems absolutely clear that this constant discrimination was an extremely important factor in the present excellence of my speech. To express this in a different way: Tension is an integral part of stuttering. The more I was able to eliminate the tension in my prolongations, the more perfectly normal my speech became. This may seem simple and not even very vital for the management of stuttering. *I must confess it has taken me years of searching to recognize the importance of my constantly discriminating between stuttered words and words on which my prolongation was altogether a voluntary one.* I felt a personal responsibility for making certain the faking plan for better management of my stuttering was successful.

Some stutterers experience complete relief from stuttering incidents when they work consistently on a faking pattern for a few days or weeks. It seems to me that is unfortunate. I experienced nothing like that. I worked steadily and consistently on my speech, and my progress was likewise slow, steady and consistent. I plodded along firmly and patiently, day by day, week after week, really year after year. Life was always interesting, fascinating, busy. I felt a new freedom as I could depend more and

156

more on being able to express myself and my thoughts. Life became more fun as I could play a more important role. There was more to delight one.

Even though a stutterer experiences fewer and fewer blocks as he fakes stuttering, he should continue faking and using whatever pattern he has chosen to aid in the management of his stuttering, for if or when he stops faking, his stuttering will return! I found then, and now more than fifty years later, I still find faking a few prolongations far preferable to stuttering even a little.

DR. BAGCHI, a young man from India who had taken his Ph.D. in psychology at Iowa, wanted to stay in America, so it was arranged for him to offer a course in Relaxation the autumn semester of 1936. During those years at Iowa every avenue for the treatment of stuttering was being explored. The relaxation class met at 11 a.m. to Tuesdays and Thursdays. Fewer than a dozen of us were enrolled. We were to have peaceful thoughts and to visualize a tranquil scene. Dr. Bagchi's method was to have us visualize progressively different parts of our own bodies. For instance, he would say in a slow, rather drawling voice, "Visualize your upper right arm." After a minute or so, "Visualize your lower right arm." We sat in a relaxed position, with closed eyes, following his direction. It took the whole period to cover the entire body. It was a form of deep relaxation. Some people in teaching relaxation will ask the subject to move or tense a part of the body, such as an arm, and then to relax that part. But Dr. Bagchi's approach was through visualization.

This enables one to locate where in one's body the tension is, and gives one a way to try to relax specific parts of the body. It is a somewhat aggressive way of attacking tension.

I well remember I would go into the class a bit tired, but when the session was over I would feel refreshed—like a new person. I recall I was somewhat surprised to observe this. It was a real privilege to have that course with Dr. Bagchi.

Edmund Jacobson M.D., wrote an excellent book, *Progressive Relaxation*. I read and studied that book. It was published in 1938, and republished in 1965 and again in 1974.

You recall I had some relaxation work at Dr. Blanton's summer school. This semester of relaxation experience with Dr. Bagchi was a splendid follow-up. It enabled me to develop a concept of relaxation, a feeling of ''well being'' when I was calm, peaceful and quiet.

The relaxation I practiced after the work with Dr. Blanton and the relaxation class with Dr. Bagchi was not a happen-so matter. It was rather the result of a conscious effort to be calm. Some of this may have come naturally after the quiet evenings at home with my parents, especially during our sod-house years. During my second year at Iowa and ever afterwards my relaxing became more an active than a passive reaction. I was conscious of trying to feel the muscles of various parts of my body take on a different muscle tone. Through the years I kept trying to keep myself as relaxed and tranquil as possible, and I still work to keep myself relaxed here in my quiet, retirement San Diego years. There is an assurance that comes with relaxation that is excellent for the stutterer, really essential for any stutterer. If one can keep relaxed, one's anxieties seem to fade away. One can scarcely be relaxed and stay anxious.

I feel that class with Dr. Bagchi has been a great benefit for me through the years. I was inclined to be anxious, tense and high strung. Now my blood pressure is rather amazing to me. In a series of twenty-seven blood pressure tests, done approximately one per week, my blood pressure ranged from 100/54 to 140/82. The median for the systolic pressure, the top number, is 116/82. The median for the diastolic pressure, the bottom number, is 112/64.

A friend, once a severe stutterer, had much relaxation work in his speech-therapy classes in the public schools of San Francisco when he was a child. Now in his early sixties, his blood pressure is comparable to mine.

I did some relaxation work in my speech therapy classes in Racine. Were I teaching speech therapy now I would regularly do some relaxation work at the beginning of each class.

THERE WERE times of uncertainty and stress because of my stuttering, but life is good, life is fascinating. I feel my daydreams helped to save me from over-anxiety. There is always the possibility of something marvelous happening to one. I could always lose myself in dreams or by reading books, but in spite of my daydreams I have proved myself a practical person.

The summer of 1935 before I went to Iowa City I felt uncertainty and anxiety, but I never had thoughts of suicide. I vaguely knew some stutterers did have suicidal thoughts. The spring of 1937 I was too busy with the courses I was taking and with working on my own stuttering to even be discouraged. Late one afternoon I stopped by Dr. Van Riper's office. He told me to sit down. Then he related the account of a young student at Iowa, a friend of his, a severe stutterer, who had folded his arms and walked out into the icy water of the Iowa River, bankfull at that season. I still feel the stress, the tension that was in Dr. Riper's voice and body as he related the tragedy to me. I was so deeply moved that when I reached my room I wrote out the incident in an attempt to calm myself.

There is no real reason for a stutterer to be depressed because of his speech. The best therapy that speech pathologists can offer is for the stutterer to work to change his stuttering pattern to a more acceptable form. A stutterer of any age may be able to find help in the management of his stuttering. The best professional speech pathologists stress wise, reasonable and practical management for stutterers, rather than hoping for a cure. Stuttering is something not to be defied, or argued with, but to be dealt with gently, and always with emphasis on relieving the accompanying tension and anxiety. To quote from Dr. Van Riper again, ". . . we can learn to accept stuttering as a problem and be willing to work to change it to a form less abnormal, and that when we do, the frequency diminishes too. It's possible to stutter and still be fluent enough to do anything."

For a stutterer to get and to keep his speech under control is, in a psychological sense, a reward equal to having earned a million dollars, and so to be rich for the rest of his life. *But the stutterer should continually acknowledge that he is a stutterer.* For one who has stuttered into adulthood to try to pass as a normal speaker is in all probability paving the way for a downfall. What is so bad about being a stutterer after all—if you have even serviceable speech? It is far better to acknowledge being a stutterer, whether or not one shows actual manifestations, than to try to pass as a normal speaker, and stutter even a little now and then. It must be difficult for a normal-speaking person to realize what a tremendous victory it is for an adult stutterer to achieve and keep serviceable speech.

FROM BEING a lonely little girl with very limited horizons, I was gaining some mastery over my stuttering. With more dependable speech some of my dreams might materialize. Unimagined possibilities could open for me. Let me say again, what I have accomplished any stutterer should be able to do if he will just keep on trying. Once one has hitched one's wagon to a star there can be no faltering.

MY SECOND WINTER at the University of Iowa, 1936-37, went along well. I was working on my speech, keeping it good. I was most fortunate in the exact years I was at Iowa. Had I been there two years earlier or two years later Dr. Van Riper's help would not have been available. Dr. Bagchi offered the relaxation class but once, so I would have missed that. Some of the good things that came to me were purely by chance. I had obtained the real thing I went to Iowa for—help with my speech. That is, I had learned how to help myself. I would have to work on my stuttering for many years, possibly the remainder of my life, but by that time I knew how to do that, and I knew how to be patient! I realized that the more I worked on my stuttering the fewer stuttering incidents I experienced.

My grades were good, but I was discouraged by the

head of the speech pathology department from going on at Iowa. I wrote to Dr. Blanton of the turn my fortunes were taking. He contacted Dr. Robert West at the University of Wisconsin. Some years earlier Dr. Blanton had organized the speech pathology work at the University of Wisconsin and over the state of Wisconsin. At that time Dr. West was Dr. Blanton's assistant. When Dr. Blanton left Wisconsin, Dr. West became the head of the Speech Pathology Department. Dr. West would welcome me at Wisconsin. So in June 1937 I went to Madison. In September a stuttering case was assigned to me. Andrew Anderson was a tall, slender lad with an extremely severe stutter. He looked pathetic. He was a junior in the university. His first two years were at a small college in Minnesota. When I asked about friends, Andrew indicated he had none at the university. After a few meetings with Andrew, almost in desperation, I asked if there were anyone at whom he could smile—in class or elsewhere. He agreed to try.

Andrew had been in speech therapy classes in Minnesota in grade school, and he had a therapist at the college he attended in Minnesota. He had pleasant memories of his therapists and of speech correction classes, but his stuttering was as severe as any I have ever seen. As I think back why should Andrew have any hope when he was assigned a new clinician at Madison? That clinician, Ida Whitten, also a stutterer!

Andrew's stuttering was so severe and he looked so sad, I was very gentle with him. During our first meetings I told him what had helped me, and I demonstrated repeatedly how I had worked on my speech. My stuttering was still such that I needed to use prolongations in all my

162

talking. I asked Andrew to try prolonging some sounds in his first meetings with me, and I asked him if he could do some work like that at home evenings. Note I made no demands, I asked him if he could do certain things. I gently asked him if he could practice prolonging sounds in some words at home.

During the third week Andrew reported he had found someone at the university with whom he could talk a little. I can still see the expression on his face. A bit of hope. So he began working on his stuttering—doing the things that had helped me. He was rooming with relatives of his family. The lady came for a conference. She or someone in the family could listen to Andrew read aloud every day, that is as he prolonged vowel sounds in his oral reading. Andrew reported making more acquaintances he could talk with and so advertise his stuttering as he practiced prolonging sounds.

But this account of my work with Andrew sounds too easy. I was not at all certain how his speech was really progressing. I did everything I could think of to keep him working regularly on reading aloud at the house where he roomed and to keep him talking to people about his speech, using prolongations all the time. I am certain I used prolongations in my own speech all the time when I talked with him—I had to use them. I made no demands, I was always gentle in my urging him to do all the things that experience had taught me could help. I often spoke about the university courses he was taking and urged him to try his best to do well. The relatives where Andrew roomed and his parents seemed to be using their influence to keep him working on his speech, especially after he began to improve, that is to manage his stuttering better.

As the weeks went by, Andrew seemed to be making
very satisfactory progress with his speech. He looked happier. He said he was doing well in his classes. That semester
he made two A grades and two B grades. Then I learned
that the previous year he had attended the University of
Wisconsin, but that during the year his grades had gone
down. The semester I worked with Andrew he was "on
condition" at the University of Wisconsin.

By the middle of the spring semester Andrew was a
transformed person. His speech was amazingly free of
stuttering. The rate of his speech was perfectly normal,
neither slower nor faster than the speech of persons who
have never stuttered. It seemed too good to be true. He
became interested in a branch of science, and one of his
professors wanted him for a student assistant. As I think
back, there is a fairytale-like characteristic to Andrew's
improvement, and to mine also. He mastered his stuttering
problem sufficiently that it did not keep him from professional success, but in retrospect I now feel it might have
been better for Andrew in the long run had we made a
slower start—as Dr. Travis advised in his lectures in 1935-
36. I now feel that I should have brought it about that
Andrew choose the pattern he would use, instead of my
teaching him the pattern that had helped me. I mean, it
is more desirable for a stutterer to choose his own pattern
than to have a pattern taught to him.

ARTHUR WAS a lad I worked with some years later when
his family moved to Racine. He was an extremely severe
stutterer in fourth grade. When he blocked his entire body
seemed convulsed. He was an Engligh lad born in London
during the Second World War. His mother said "food was

164

hard to get'' and so the parents became accustomed to Arthur eating small servings. In the fourth grade he was of slighter build and not as tall as the other boys.

There was one much older brother. When this brother came to the United States, the parents and Arthur followed soon afterward. The family lived in a basement apartment near downtown.

Arthur's teacher worked with me. I taught him to prolong sounds as I did for my own speech, and his teacher encouraged him to prolong sounds in the classroom. I urged Arthur's mother to get him to read aloud to her *every evening* at home, and to prolong many vowel sounds as he read aloud.

Within a few weeks Arthur's speech was improving— then later practically normal in school, on the playground, at home. I urged the oral reading be continued, but I do not think I spoke much of how a stutterer discriminates between stuttered and non-stuttered words. I did not realize then how important that was.

Arthur's speech cleared up so very quickly it seemed enough to urge him to keep up daily oral reading at home even though his speech seemed free of stuttering. I made a special home call to urge the mother to see to it that Arthur did the daily oral reading at home, but I realized the mother was an indecisive woman and that at home Arthur—so to speak—''ruled the roost.''

When I talked to Arthur about continuing to work on his speech and to read aloud at home and make his sounds long as he read, he would say, ''There's just nothing to work on.''

The last time I saw Arthur he was in senior high school

and stuttering severely again. I could do nothing to help him. He was in a school where I was not working.

SOME OF THE SUMMERS I was with Dr Blanton I worked with young-adult stutterers. I tried to teach them the prolongation pattern that had helped me. I showed them how I prolonged sounds, mostly vowel sounds, and I tried to get them to discriminate carefully between stuttered and non-stuttered prolongations, but I did not insist that as they read aloud they mark with different colored pencils the stuttered and non-stuttered prolongations. At that time I had no idea of just how vital that discrimination might be.

The speech of those young-adult stutterers usually improved markedly within a few weeks or even days. It is important that a stutterer not feel punished by what he is doing to improve his speech, so I tried to help them as quickly as possible. Of course I always warned them and their families about relapses.

I tried to keep in touch with those young-adult stutterers for a time and one of them I did see when he was near retirement age. There was no overt evidence of stuttering, but his speech was painfully slow. It seems probable that when he felt a stutter coming, he simply waited until the stuttering sensation passed. He possessed a great deal of control or he could not have done that. In contrast, in my own speech I used prolongations of vowel sounds *before* I felt real stuttering. My own speech has always been at completely normal tempo.

THE MORAL of all this is that the stutterer will relapse unless he continues to work *every day*, perhaps every

166

waking hour, to keep his speech good. There probably is no cure for the stutterer who has stuttered severely even into his elementary school years. With older stutterers the best help, I am convinced, is careful discrimination between stuttered and non-stuttered words, as I practiced on my own speech. This should enable a stutterer to keep his speech good, but once a severe stutterer in school, he should never, never cease to work daily to keep his speech good, even if his stutter is in abeyance, and even if he lives to be ninety. But surely even daily work on a stutter is better than just stuttering with no way to help himself. Dr. Wendell Johnson used his "bounce pattern" as long as he lived.

This is my thinking—fifty years after I came upon Dr. Van Riper in the old psychology building at Iowa the autumn of 1935. That was when Dr. Van gave me the 200 speech-situation assignment.

I FELT a responsibility to begin repaying the educational loan that had enabled me to go to Iowa. I learned there was a vacancy in the speech therapy department in the public schools at Racine, Wisconsin, so I wrote a short letter asking if I might go to Racine for an interview. In that letter I stated that I was a stutterer, and that I had been working on my speech at Iowa. I received an answer by return mail stating that Mr. Giese, the superintendent, would see me any time I could get to Racine, so I went over that same day. When I arrived in Racine I telephoned the Superintendent's office. By that time I could make a telephone call, but no doubt I did plenty of prolonging of sounds.

Mr. Giese was in a meeting that would go on into the evening, but his secretary would get my message to him. So after his meeting Mr. Giese did come to the Racine Hotel. He was then past middle age, a jovial, kindly person with a most hearty chuckle. We talked and talked. I told him a good deal of my story and I demonstrated in detail how I was working on my speech. He offered me the position.

When I got back to Madison I hastened to go tell Dr. West that I had the position. He said, "Oh, yes, I know. Mr. Giese called this morning to find out if all Ida Whitten had told him was true." No one told me to write of my stuttering in my letter of inquiry or to speak of it in detail in the interview with the superintendent, but I knew that was the only thing to do—to have nothing to hide!

CHAPTER 14

SPEECH THERAPY AT RACINE

IT WAS near the end of January, 1938, when the semester at the University of Wisconsin was finished and I could go to Racine. I had a ride over on a Sunday afternoon, and stayed that first night at a house on the lake front. The next morning at breakfast as I looked out the big picture window I had my first real view of Lake Michigan. Remember it was late January, cold and icy. I had never seen anything in any way comparable with the view I beheld: As far as I could see many thin streams of condensing water vapor were rising from the lake. This phenomenon of condensing vapor, in the Arctic sometimes spoken of as "sea smoke," occurs when the air is colder than the water. In a way the lake resembled an enormous caldron of boiling water with thin spirals of steam rising from all over it; or in a different figure it was as though thin streams of smoke were rising from innumerable small fires spread over the surface of the water. Cold air over warmer water causes water vapors to condense into small cloud forms. Some years later with my own camera I took excellent pictures of this phenomenon. This view, my first morning in Racine by Lake Michigan, was a memory picture to treasure.

THE FIRST DAY of school passed someway. I tried to follow my predecessor's schedule. After school I needed to find a room where I could live. The Durgin family had a small but adequate room. What did I like for breakfast?

"Oatmeal." I'm certain I used a prolongation on the vowel for I needed to prolong some sounds in everything I said, especially before strangers.

"Well, Mr. Durgin would like hot cereal, too."

The Durgins were an interesting family. Mr. Durgin was on the school board, the two daughters were junior and senior high school age. From my room upstairs I could hear when, some evenings, Mrs. Durgin played classical music on her baby-grand piano. She was also a birder. Sometimes while I ate my breakfast she would report on the birds far back in the yard and what they were doing. The Durgins had binoculars, so for the first time in my life I got to *see* the birds.

Fate provided marvelously for me in many ways. I could get dinner at the Chadwick home just down the street. Mr. Chadwick as city engineer kept us aware that the city water was excellent, that it was soft water from Lake Michigan. Both the Durgins and the Chadwicks were appreciative of antiques. Now my apartment is furnished with antiques which, over the years, I purchased from the original owners.

There were two of us speech correction teachers or speech therapists but I was the only one who stuttered, perhaps I was the only teacher in Wisconsin who stuttered.

170

We speech teachers rode the city buses, for then few beginning teachers could afford a car. A weekly bus pass cost one dollar and at the end of the school year the city reimbursed us for our bus passes. I had to learn the bus routes and how to get to each school for which I was scheduled. Racine was more than twice as large as Lincoln or Iowa City, the only cities I knew, and I had not needed to travel around in those university cities. I was so involved each day with getting to the school where I was scheduled, I had not much opportunity to even look at the water of Lake Michigan.

Racine was then an industrial city of 60,000. Smoke stacks intermittently belched forth enormous, fantastic-shaped masses of black smoke over the city. The Case Company, then the largest manufacturer of farm machinery in the United States, employed large numbers of poorly-paid factory workers, some of whom lived in factory-owned houses.

In my school work I followed the daily schedule of my predecessor, thus I worked in five elementary schools. For example I was at Knapp School on Monday and Thursday mornings, and at Howell School on Monday and Thursday afternoons. Wednesday morning was the one time I was at Franklin School, and Wednesday afternoon I was to make five home calls. My schedule in a school was divided into periods of twenty-five to thirty minutes. The speech problems we saw were delayed speech, articulatory cases such as incorrect S-Z or R sounds, and an occasional child who stuttered. We tried to take the children at such times as were most convenient for their classroom teachers.

I needed to learn the names of the classroom teachers in those five schools in which I worked. There were nearly

171

a hundred pupils with speech problems, and of course I needed to learn their names and each child's speech needs. During my first weeks in Racine I did my best to have individual conferences with the teachers and to explain the speech needs of each pupil in my classes to the teacher so she might also help the pupil with his speech. Several teachers said I was the only speech therapist who had ever held conferences with them regarding the speech needs of their pupils.

Those first weeks in Racine were a most interesting, challenging, busy time for me, and it was bitterly cold— the sidewalks icy. Every sentence I said I needed to use my speech pattern, that is to prolong some vowel sounds in my speaking. I usually tried to begin a sentence with words on which I could easily use prolongations. I felt very strongly that was a time I must keep my speech serviceable and as acceptable as possible. It is distracting and disintegrating to stutter, but I had worked so consistently on prolonging sounds and I was so accustomed to using drawn-out vowels that it usually did not cause disintegration of my thought processes, but as I have explained before, each prolongation of sound required a decision on my part. The prolongations never in any way have become automatic, even now after fifty years.

After several weeks I began to feel a need to contact some of the mothers, so in speech class we would talk about how nice it would be to have a mother visit, and we would plan that sometime that spring each child's mother would be invited. Thus a child was usually pleased to have his mother invited, but if I sensed any reluctance in a child we just waited a few weeks and invited a different child's mother to come visit. Then I would send a note

172

home with the child whose mother we were inviting. I specified a definite day and hour for her visit. Eventually I must master the telephone situation, but for the time I mostly sent notes. At that time many families did not have a telephone. I invited only one mother at a time to visit a class, and usually but one mother for the half-day I was in the building. There was a little additional stress on me when a mother came. At that time not many women worked outside their homes. After a mother visited I tried to send practice material home with which the mother could help and encourage her child. Parents want the best for their children, so it was a real benefit to have the mothers visit.

In some of the schools the space designated for speech correction classes was poorly heated and unattractive. Since speech classes met but twice per week, sometimes we were given the least desirable space in the building. The school enrollment was high, so every room was in use. A nurse was in a school for at least a short time each day, so she was given a more pleasant space than speech correction. For the time being at least, the only thing to do was say as little as possible about the undesirable aspects, and do the very best possible work in the space we had. I tried to locate chairs that would be fairly comfortable for the classes of various ages—six to twelve years. It was still depression time. The schools were sometimes short on essential supplies such as paper. We teachers felt concern for the nutrition of some of the children from large families.

Only two and a half years earlier I had matriculated at Iowa City. I made excellent progress in that sheltered-workshop situation, but then at Racine I was out in the world of reality and on my own. True, I was employed as a stutterer—a largely rehabilitated stutterer. For many years there was a shortage of speech therapists. It was somewhat courageous of Mr. Giese, the superintendent, to employ a teacher who stuttered. In a way he prepared the school system and the community to accept such a teacher. One thing he did was to invite me to a Chamber of Commerce Luncheon and introduce me to the group. I said two or three short sentences and of course used prolonged vowel sounds. It was splended for the public to see and hear me speak in such a situation. I owe Mr. Giese a deep debt of gratitude. I think I felt responsibility to make good for the sake of those who had employed me as well as for my own sake. I was still full of the determination and resolve that had taken me to the University of Iowa. I was aware that my speech had to keep on improving if I were to make good as a teacher in the Racine School System. Some degree of security, peace and tranquility came to my spirit. If I kept prolonging sounds, thus keeping my speech acceptable, I could go on professionally. The first year and a half seemed the most crucial, but I do not think I was ever penalized in Racine for my stuttering.

I seem not to have let myself indulge in fears, but to have exerted all my energy toward doing excellent work in the schools, and to keep working on my stuttering so my own speech even kept on improving a little. I kept remembering Dr. Wendell Johnson and some other stutterers who were advancing in their fields, but they were in universities or colleges. The public schools seemed different.

My stuttering was a constant problem to be dealt with every time I spoke. I might at any moment feel a stuttering

incident coming. The only safe way for me was to com-
mence prolonging sounds on my very first words in every
conversation, and to keep using a long sound every three
or four words. I was so accustomed to prolonging sounds
in talking that it usually did not distract my thoughts. I
prolonged sounds in talking with one of the principals,
in talking with the teachers whenever and wherever I met
one or more of them. I used long sounds whenever I met
a parent. I used slightly prolonged sounds in speaking
with the pupils in each class. I felt some concern about
prolonging sounds before the pupils for I was responsible
for them, but children are marvelous! They accepted me
with my slightly drawn-out sounds with never a question.
They were the easiest speech situations I had. Usually one
to two second prolongations were sufficient in talking with
the children. Pets and children are in general easier for
stutterers to speak with than adults. In a conversation if
I began by prolonging several vowels, I usually could
continue the conversation with fewer long sounds. I had
discovered that fact by experience at Iowa City. Also the
more I prolonged sounds the more at ease I was. Before
I went to Iowa the future had been like a black void unless
or until I could get my speech under control. Is it little
wonder that I went ahead doing things for my speech
without much fear? Doing all I could on my speech gave
me a sense of calm, of peace, even of security. Life with
the passage of time can be a great healer.

In due time the bitterly cold, icy weeks gave way to
an inspiring spring. It seemed there were a few spring
flowers around even the poorest-looking homes. An occasional cardinal poured forth his series of clear, slurred
whistles from the very top of the tallest tree. Before the

leaves grew, when he flew, I could recognize the bird as a cardinal by its flash of brilliant red across the sky. After the long winter, a Wisconsin spring, especially on the shore of Lake Michigan, has a marvelously invigorating effect on one. I began to feel a little assurance that I was doing the right things with the pupils for they were progressing and many of the teachers were friendly and cooperative. I came to enjoy my association with the teachers in the buildings in which I worked. Gradually the teachers in some of the schools let me attend their school parties and be one of them. (After these pages about my experiences with stuttering fifty years ago, it is a relief to let my thoughts wander. At the Pacific the tide was out this morning. There were only low waves rolling in. Just before a wave crests, even a low wave, in the advancing wall of water there are lovely bright greens shading to blues. Even on a dark day when the Pacific may appear menacing, there are these delicate shadings of greens and blues, but just for the moment before the wave crests. To me those moments of bright, clear color represent Sincerity, Courage and Hope.)

Stutterers dread telephone calls! I recall I tried to make the few telephone calls I did to the mothers of my pupils something of an adventure. I would talk to a child about calling his mother so he would not be surprised or fearful. Sometimes I sent a short note. Thus the mother would know I was going to telephone. After I dialed and she answered I might begin "Thi---s is the spee----ch co---rrection tea---cher." That seemed easier than to start with "Thi---s is Mi----ss Whi-----tten," only the plosive sound at the beginning of *teacher* might be a real problem. The prolongations are easier than the soft or incomplete chosures, at least that was the case for me. On some occasions, I well recall, I simply left off the *t* sound of *teacher* and said "ea----cher." One could do that on the telephone without it being as obvious as when face to face. I used all the schemes I knew or could think of. I tried using some of the public speaking techniques I had learned from my mother, that is projecting my voice so I could easily be heard all over the auditorium before loud-speaking equipment was in common use. In a way it was a different tone of voice.

While I was attending the University of Nebraska I managed to have some vocal music lessons. I learned to use diaphragm breathing to sustain tone control. I tried to use that in my telephone calls. I would think exactly how I was going to begin and to choose words on which I could use prolongations. Those were real life situations. It was far harder than going out and doing speech situations in Iowa City. I felt a tremendous challenge to some-way succeed. Racine was an excellent teaching position. I wanted to continue there. I realized that the more I used prolongations the better my speech would be. After per-haps fifteen years in Racine I became sufficiently at ease with my speech to begin enjoying doing easy telephone calls. Some calls are far easier than others for stutterers.

It took me awhile to learn how to make home visits. It was best if I wrote a note or did a telephone call so the mother would know I was coming. When I arrived at the home I found it was best to sit down, lean back in the chair, and above all to keep calm and relaxed. I would give the mother my full attention and visit with her, but let her take the lead. I tried to speak with a rather slow, gentle tone of voice. If I did this and if there were small

children in the home, often they would come to me—
and the pets would come. I needed to enlist the coop-
eration of the mother. If she liked me, she was more likely,
I found, to help her child with speech.

I especially recall one visit. "I can't get Roy to work
on his speech. It's no use for me to try." Those were
almost the first words the mother of one junior high school
lad said when I called at her home. I thought, well that
is that, but it was a warm spring day and I was tired, so
I just sat awhile and visited with the mother. "Roy will
just have to work on his speech. I will see that he does."
Those were the mother's words when I was bidding her
good-bye; and Roy's speech did improve.

I WAS qualified for membership in ASHA (The American
Speech and Hearing Association) when I went to Racine,
so I soon became a member. Whenever we were given
time I would go to the National Convention which was
often held at Thanksgiving time. I found it inspirational
to attend those meetings and to meet the leaders in the
field of Speech Pathology. I became aware that some of
the leaders were watching my speech progress—Dr. West
with whom I had studied at Wisconsin, and even Dr.
Bryngelson at the University of Minnesota. That put responsibility on me to see that my speech kept improving.
Of course I knew Dr. Blanton and Dr. Van Riper were
concerned with my progress.

DURING MY EARLY YEARS in Racine the Second World
War was in progress. I wanted to do something to help.
I inquired at the USO. There seemed no need for one of
my age there, but then I was at the USO an evening or

two, and there I found a service I could render. I sewed buttons on the service men's coats. Many times the buttons were in the jacket pockets, but I bought a few buttons for those instances when the buttons were lost. Sometimes when a lad came to get his coat he would think his coat could not be his because all the buttons were on it.

I realized that to be most effective as a speech therapist in the city schools I needed to be a part of the community life, and I needed to be happy in my work and to feel it was rewarding work I was doing. Soon after I went to Racine I joined AAUW (The American Association of University Women). That brought me into contact with some of the women of the community who were leaders. I realize now I needed to become a more adequate individual, a better socially adjusted person in the community. I needed the stimulation of association with keen minds away from the school system. Remember that in treating stuttering one must treat the whole person, not just the stutter.

I attended the book section of AAUW. Various ones volunteered to give book reviews. After I had been in Racine nearly fifteen years I found a book I wanted to share, so I offered to give a review. Those women seemed so sure of themselves and so well established, it was difficult for me to use prolongations before them. But I had to use my prolongations or stutter, so I used the prolongations. My review was rather short but it was acceptable. It was quite difficult then for me to read aloud before such a group. Now in San Diego I can read aloud easily and well before any group, but I am careful to start off with prolongations.

The Racine branch of AAUW had the custom of calling

179

the members once a month to remind them of the general meeting. It was after I had been in Racine for twenty-five years that I finally felt secure enough with my speech to volunteer to be one of those who did telephone calls. That was a different kind of speech experience, for some of those women impressed me as being very sophisticated individuals. The husband might answer and I would have to ask for the wife and say a specific name. That was difficult, but I finally mastered that, too. The more I branched out in speech situations and in telephone calls, the easier speech became. As I think back it was a matter of conquering speech situations one at a time. Now I can thoroughly enjoy any and all telephone calls. There is no quick easy help for an adult stutterer, but there is help if one will work, and work persistently, to modify the stuttering symptom.

RACINE is thirty miles south of Milwaukee. Soon I began going to plays and concerts there. I even heard Vladimir Horowitz—the great Russian-born pianist—there once. There were cultural privileges such as I had never known, or dreamed of, before.

Racine is seventy miles north of Chicago, or an hour and ten minutes on the train. At that time the train fare between Racine and Chicago was a dollar each way. It was easy to go in on the train, shop a bit, have lunch at Marshall Field's and go to a play. Many of the plays were just from Broadway, or on the way to Broadway. Also there were, from time to time, special exhibits at the Art Institute. I well recall the extensive exhibits of the work of Matisse and of Picasso. I got quite an art education by seeing such exhibits as those. When the big Picasso exhibit

180

was there I went in three times to see it. In between trips I read a good deal about Picasso and his art. It seems to me I could not have been better located to take advantage of cultural events. All this helped to form me into a more adequate and a more interesting person.

I HAD grown up in western Kansas far from any lakes or large rivers. The lakes at Madison are scenic and an integral part of the life there, but it was not until Racine that I was near a large body of water. My first years in Racine I may have been a bit fearful of Lake Michigan. The Lake influences the climate to a considerable degree. In winter it is often colder near the Lake. If one drives seven miles or so away from the Lake one notices a difference in the temperature—winter or summer. Soon I began to sense the affection and regard Raciners felt for the Lake. Anyone living near that great beautiful and powerful body of water must be more or less influenced by it. It is eighty miles across in some places. Gradually I became aware of the beauty, the charm, and fascination the Lake can hold for one, and so in time I became very fond of Lake Michigan, and I came to fully appreciate its beauty and its particular charm. Lake Michigan, like an ocean, is different every day, it even seems to have moods.

MY MEMORY keeps going back to a curious reaction I became aware of after I had been in Racine for perhaps ten years. "If I am very good and kind and do things for the teachers and people I work closely with maybe they will not hurt me." This exact wording is necessary to express this bit from the preconscious. The origin of this strange memory seems to go far back to threads, roots in my earliest childhood. This may even be related to my need for approval from the adults around me—my parents, then teachers and later persons in influential positions. I have a persistent, although very dim impression, that the feeling "If I am very good maybe they won't hurt me" goes way back to my earliest childhood days, but I was never spanked. One disapproving word or look was real punishment, I was so sensitive. When children play together, sometimes "rough and tumble," they learn to get along together and an individual, even when small, learns to hold his own with others. But I grew up practically an only child, a loved, humored, petted child. The playtimes of nursery and pre-school years are vital for small children.

One autumn in Racine, after I had my own apartment, I baked applesauce cakes, took them to school, and served cake and coffee to the teachers at recess or after school before a teachers' meeting. You remember I worked in five schools, so this was quite a project, however after that most of the teachers were noticeably warmer toward me and more friendly.

It is possible that what seems to me my unusual sensitiveness may have been a sensitivity that pervaded my entire body-system, possibly an inherited factor. In mid-life my mother began to have hay-fever and suffered from that every autumn the remainder of her life. In my later years I have difficulty with various foods. It seems this unusual sensitivity might possibly have had a relationship to irregularities in my early speech, and that these irregularities were interpreted and reacted to as stuttering.

A child of one or two years is so small, fragile and weak compared with the adults around him, one can understand how a shy, fearful little child could actually

182

be fearful of what could happen to him if he should displease those adults. An only child might be more fearful than when there are small playfellows.

This reaction "If I am very, very good and do things for them maybe they won't hurt me" had not been expressed in words or thoughts in my consciousness before I was in Racine, but something of this feeling had been in my consciousness for a long, long time, possibly some such feeling since my earliest childhood. In the labyrinth of my very earliest memories it vaguely seems this "Maybe they won't hurt me" might be associated or reinforced with the incident in Chapter 3 when my father said, "You sit over there. You're heavy," and he put me over in a chair beside his.

For many years I have subscribed to the weekday *New York Times,* not the National Edition, but the edition from New York City. I have long felt a need, a compulsion to share, to pass my copies of the *Times* on to neighbors or acquaintances who may enjoy them. In some cases this is an aid in making friends. It is also almost a need, a compulsion for me here in San Diego to share my roses and gardenias with chosen neighbors and friends. This may echo back to the "Maybe people won't hurt me if I am very good and kind."

CHAPTER 15

FOREIGN TRAVEL

AFTER TWENTY-TWO YEARS in Racine my position there was established. The teachers and parents trusted me and depended on me to help the children who needed speech help. My own speech was excellent. I was a part of several social groups in the schools in which I worked. Since my two years of teaching at Aberdeen, the thought had been in my mind that sometime I should travel abroad. I wondered what could be so wonderful, so splendid about foreign travel. My dear friend from my Aberdeen days, Mrs. Garvin, had studied abroad and in later years traveled to Europe, every summer.

As I think back, it seems I was curious as to what could be so interesting about foreign travel. You remember my curiosity about the horsehairs in the puddles of water. It seemed to me I should take a trip abroad and so find out the value, the interest for myself. Did life hold more enrichment than I had yet sampled?

I knew the college at Aberdeen sponsored some foreign trips, and that one could earn college credits that way. The Racine school system had made a requirement that all teachers earn three credits every five years, so a trip would be a different way of earning those credits. On inquiry I learned that Professor Tostlebe, whom I knew, would lead a four-week geography trip to Latin America.

I sent for my Passport. I can still feel some of the excitement of that time. I felt I should have a camera for I wanted to share the trip with my family and special friends. When I went to look at cameras, the idealism in me manifested itself in that I asked, "Will that camera take the best slides?" Finally I decided on a Leica, a fine German-made camera.

So in July 1960 I joined the tour at Houston, Texas. Our planes on that trip were not jets but lower-flying planes so one could see quite well the rivers, lakes, mountains, volcanoes, and take pictures out the windows. One could even see the hardened trails of lava sometimes left on a mountain side after volcanic eruptions. As we took off from Houston at sunset the sky was at its most colorful moment. All the rainbow colors were blended into a dazzingly beautiful sky-painting as viewed from our vantage point in the air. I took pictures of the sunset through the airplane window. Such a sky seemed a good omen for our trip.

Mr. Tostlebe had assembled a book of more than a hundred pages and had it mimeographed. That was before the time of modern copying machines. So we were studying about the rivers, lakes, mountains and volcanoes along the way on our geography tour for we had to pass a written test at the end. Our first stop was Mexico City at some 7370 feet elevation. (Denver, our mile-high city, is 5280 feet.) We visited the Aztec remains near by, then Guayaquil in Ecuador. Such enormous quantities of bananas ready to be shipped! Then Quito at 9300 feet elevation.

The day we visited the Equatorial Monument, a bit north of Quito, I wore a light-weight coat all day. It was cool at the equator because of the elevation.

Next the fine old Spanish city, Lima, Peru, with the great Prehistoric Museum. I can still picture the fine, intricate iron-grill work we saw in many places in the city. We flew to Cuzco, the old Inca Capitol, at 11,000 feet elevation, more than two miles high. Most of us on the tour were more or less affected by that altitude. Next on to Machu Picchu, the ancient Inca fortress with the beautifully fitted one to three ton stones.

Then on to Sao Paulo, Brazil, that great modern, commercial city which reminded me a bit of Chicago. I loved the Kansas prairies, but I had learned to thrill to the heartbeat of a great city. After that on to Rio de Janeiro with a side trip to the then new Brasilia.

(As I write this in my San Diego home this May the Jacaranda trees are in bloom here near the coast. Jacaranda is a Portuguese word. There are many jacarandas in and near Rio de Janeiro. They have lovely, delicate, dragon-like, lavender blooms.)

I saw the faces of the people of Latin and South America—children and adults. I saw their faces in my pictures and in my memory, most of them of mixed blood for the early settlers inter-married with the Indians. In Brazil the early Portuguese settlers brought African slaves, as in the United States, but the Portuguese did not bring their wives to the new world. Since this trip, I have been much interested in Latin and South American affairs, especially for Brazil and Peru where we spent the most time.

The following winter I read whatever books I could

187

find about the people and history of the areas we had visited. This was the beginning of what was to be the equal of another college education for me. I had taken pictures all along the way, so I had 300 slides, and they were excellent pictures. I got a projector and a screen so I could show my slides to small groups of friends and later to larger groups. I could not have done anything that would have been better for my speech! Oh yes, I used prolongations! That was my insurance for good speech.

FRANCE and the French language had long held fascination for me. The early spring of 1959 Mr. Johnson, the young Professor of French at the University of Wisconsin in Racine, agreed to give me French lessons. I got the French text he recommended: *Basic Conversational French* by Harris and Lévèque. How I did study that book, every evening! I had great difficulty understanding and learning the French pronunciation. I seem not to have a gift for learning languages. My stuttering manifested itself in full force. It was just as severe trying to pronounce the French as it had been in the high school and college Latin classes many years earlier, but my English speech remained excellent.

Perhaps it was my work in teaching correct sound production to the children at school that increased my desire to produce the French with quite perfect enunciation. My personal need for perfection in the pronunciation of the French may have exaggerated the stuttering. Anyway, my stuttering was a real handicap, and I could not seem to master it even in practicing the French at home.

I kept on studying and trying. Professor Johnson, I'm certain, felt sorry for me and tried to understand. There is a certain rhythm in spoken French. Mr. Johnson would say a phrase or sentence in French, that I should repeat after him. I could not remember the French pronunciation well enough to practice it much at home. If I could have practiced the French aloud at home it seems I should have been able to fit my prolongations into the oral French. As the months went by, I did learn a number of French phrases and sentences. As I recall I could fit a few prolongations into those. It seems to me now that at the time I was studying French I might not have had nearly so much stuttering had I been studying German instead of French. I might have used my prolongations more easily on the German where all the letters are pronounced.

The spring of 1961 I answered an advertisement for Study Abroad. There was a plan to study French in Paris for a month. I went on that Tour, and I was in a French class with a French teacher. I didn't learn much French, but it was marvelous to be a month in Paris.

There was a two-day week-end trip to Mount St. Michael (Le Mont St. Michel). St. Michael began as an abbey built on a great rock on the coast, and was added to from time to time until it became the great monument it is today. At the place where we spent the night there were post cards showing sheep grazing on the tidal salt flats beside St. Michael. The next day when we visited St. Michael I looked for the sheep, but there were none. Then I thought of my binoculars. There the sheep were. I put my telephoto lens in my Leica camera and took pictures of the sheep I could not see without my binoculars. In due time when the film was developed I had excellent pictures of those sheep grazing on the tidal salt flats.

Some of the theatres in Paris are small, and the admission at that time only a few francs. I saw Sartre's ''No

Exit'' in one of those small theatres. I got a copy of the play in English so I might follow it in French. I still feel the charm of the way that play was produced. The three characters are in the next world, and it is not Heaven. It is quite warm where they are.

Of course I visited the Louvre, and I discovered the relatively small Jeu de Paume collection where the paintings of the impressionists are hung, paintings done by Monet, Cezanne, Manet, Seurat, Toulouse-Lautrec and others. Whenever I was in Paris after that, I visited the Jeu de Paume.

Then there was a two-week bus tour around France. I had read articles in the *New York Times* about the prehistoric paintings in the Lascaux Cave, discovered in 1940. We went through that cave. Such an experience to see with my own eyes "The Hall of the Bulls" and the "Frieze of Stags," to name only two. I bought slides of those cave paintings. The following winter, after I had read Abbé Breuil's scholarly book on the paintings, I showed those slides to an AAUW group and discussed the slides in some detail. My speech was better than for the book review I had given some years earlier.

Our bus tour of France took us along the route Napoleon took when he went to Corsica. At Nice some of us took a taxi to the charming village, Vence, to view the Chapel that Matisse decorated for the Sisters who took care of him when he was ill there. That Chapel is a gem to remember. I looked and looked that I might later recall the peace and beauty of those paintings.

I gazed—and gazed—but little thought
What wealth the show to me had brought;
"The Daffodils" by William Wordsworth.

190

I'm not certain when I learned how interesting it is to go into a community and meet new people, some of whom may become real friends. So it is with a Tour or Seminar. I still have friends from my trips abroad.

The pure joy of that time has stayed with me, to learn and to experience all I saw that summer. How that enriched my memories. Yes, I might still have an occasional slight stutter. The joy of knowing was to be ever with me. My experiences of the past enabled me to gain the utmost from that summer. How thrilling it is to be in Paris!

My associates in Racine knew me as a dependable speech therapist. After my foreign travel began, they saw me in a different role. I was a more important person, a more interesting individual. Their attitudes toward me reflected the growth travel and a wide experience had brought to me. Also, I think my growth in experience was reflected in my speech. I was a more important person in my own view. This had a positive effect on my speech. There was less and less stuttering. As I write this in retrospect, I realize I was the same person with the same devotion to my work, but I had grown in experience.

Back in Racine I continued my study of French. Despite all my efforts my progress in French was painfully slow. Mr. Johnson was patient for many months, but finally he became discouraged with what seemed to him my lack of rapid progress, and in addition to that my severe stuttering, so the lessons were discontinued, but I kept trying on my own to learn a little more French.

THE SPRING of 1962 I answered an advertisement for a Seminar to Russia. Dr. Jerome Davis, a retired Yale Professor, was leading a tour to Russia. The name of the seminar was Promoting Enduring Peace. My letter to Dr. Davis indicated I was fearful about going into Russia. He wrote me he would take me to visit in any apartment on any street I chose. Dr. Davis knew Russian. He had worked with the YMCA in Russia during both world wars. Some have suggested those visits were arranged, but they could not have been. I went with him many times. You remember I was accustomed to doing professional home calls.

When Dr. Davis' knock at a Russian apartment was answered, he would draw himself up to his full height and say in Russian, "We are Americans. We would so like to see a Russian apartment." Dr. Davis was a person of considerable personal charm. Practically always we were admitted. We would sit and visit for fifteen minutes or so. Dr. Davis would ask about their rent, utility bills, health care, etc.

Dr. Davis wanted every one in the Seminar to have an opportunity to visit in a Russian apartment. The following incident comes to my mind. One afternoon when there were six of us, someone pointed to the apartment building we should enter. We entered an elevator and someone called out "Sixth floor." When Dr. Davis knocked on the nearest apartment door, a middle-aged lady opened the door. She was a bit surprised and uncertain what to do, so Dr. Davis knocked on a near-by door. A big Russian man opened the door. In response to Dr. Davis, the Russian answered in his great, hearty welcoming voice, "Come in, come in."

As we entered the man's apartment I glanced at the lady who had hesitated to let us into her apartment. Such a crestfallen look on her face. She had missed something really interesting!

192

When out tour was at Sochi, a resort area half way down the east coast of the Black Sea, Dr. Davis introduced me to a Russian teacher who wanted to correspond with an American teacher. Valentina taught English in a Russian school corresponding to our junior high, so we write in English. She with her husband, a mathematics teacher, their fourteen year old daughter Elizabeth, and Valentina's mother lived at Veronezh, a city some 150 miles south and a bit east of Moscow, or 100 miles northeast of Kharkov. Now Valentina's husband and mother are no longer living, and she has been retired since she was age fifty-five. Elizabeth, her husband Yuri, and their nineteen year old son, Alec, live with Valentina in her apartment which has four large rooms with bath. Alec is being married soon. Valentina has a telephone in her name. Elizabeth and Yuri graduated from the Medical Institute and they are spoken of as doctors, but they are not doctors in our sense of the word. For these twenty-five years Valentina and I have exchanged six to eight letters per year. I feel she is quite a close friend.

I must have been in twenty-five Russian homes. After that trip my experiences and the pictures I had taken were of interest to a wider group.

IN 1963 I went on a Bird Watching Tour. We started in the north of England, then north through Norway. At North Cape we saw the midnight sun. There was light enough at midnight to see to walk, but scarcely enough to read by. Even at mid-day it was a bit like twilight. The next day in that bleak, dismal, desolate area far beyond the Arctic Circle we visited a camp where the Lapps with their reindeer live. Those people seemed as deprived as their surroundings were gloomy.

On that Bird Tour we saw and heard many of the birds mentioned in literature. I still thrill to the memory of the Black Bird I heard singing outside the window of my room in the north of England late one afternoon. The European Black Bird is very like our American Robin in song and habits. The birds of Europe, in the main, are entirely different from the birds of America.

In Norway we saw two Stave Churches, that is churches built of wood long before the Christian era. Once there were several hundred of these. The startling thing is to see dragon heads and crosses on the same structures. Even when the crosses were added, indicating Christianity was accepted, the carved dragons' heads were retained—just to assure protection from evil spirits.

After the month-long tour of the Birds of Europe, I flew alone to Greece for another month-long tour. I had had a course in Ancient History in college so I knew something of fifth century B.C. Greece. Professor Constantine, our leader, was a professor of the ancient Greek language.

I arrived in Athens the evening before the day I was to meet Professor Constantine and the tour members. I was eager to see something of the ancient monuments. A hotel official suggested I go up on the roof of the hotel where there was a look-out area, so I did that. I looked all around, but the horizon was dark. I kept turning around and looking. Then I saw the Parthenon illumunated by flood lights! The flood lights were alternately off and on. I watched for some minutes. Another fine memory-picture was stored up in my mind. Of course that

194

view whetted my eagerness for what we were to see of Greece.

Our first stop was Olympia where the Olympic Games began. The cicadas were so noisy one could not but be aware of them. Their shrill notes blended with the wind through the trees. Cicadas are a kind of locust.

We visited Mycenae where Agamemnon and Clytemnestra played out their destined roles. Mycenae is just a ruin now, so one needed to call forth much imagination to appreciate it.

We flew to Crete where Sir Arthur Evans had in part restored the Palace of Knossos. There one could see things much as they had been in 1500 B.C. when the Minoan civilization was in full flower. That was the most delightful of the ancient places we saw, I think. The walls of the ancient palace had been covered with frescoes. Those frescoes had fallen from the walls, but the colors had fallen in a pattern so it had been possible to restore the frescoes to their original brilliance with a good deal of accuracy.

I looked forward to Delphi where the oracles had influenced the fate of the Greek Nation so long ago. I especially enjoyed our stay in Athens. Several times I visited the huge National Museum where excavated objects from the great civilizations of ancient Greece are on exhibit.

We stayed at the Grand Bretagne Hotel. They served excellent watermelon, almost equal to the best Kansas watermelon.

THE AMERICAN National Education Association sponsored a six week exchange tour with Germany. In 1964 I went on that very special tour. For three weeks we were guests of the German government and had opportunity to visit with German teachers. In our discussions we learned the schools were having difficulty deciding just what should be taught to the pupils regarding the Holocaust and the persecution of the Jews. That was one of my very best tours, however I could never quite forget we had fought against the Germans in two world wars, but I had also to remember we had fought the English in our own Revolutionary War. I was entertained in two German homes. (In France I was never in a French home.)

MY 1965 TOUR was to England. The previous year was the four hundreth birthday of Shakespeare. We were taken to Stratford where we saw several Shakespeare plays. Then we visited the great Cathedrals of England and some of the great country houses which are now under the National Trust. I was thrilled with the Cathedrals and the fine old stained-glass windows. I would enjoy visiting those magnificent Cathedrals every summer. On that tour we also had opportunity to visit with some of the teachers of England.

IN 1966 I made a return visit to Russia, again with Dr. Davis as the leader. It was much the same as the 1962 tour. After Russia we stopped in Budapest, Hungary. That was far different from Russia even though Hungary is in the Soviet block. Evenings there was a good orchestra in the dining room of the hotel. The expression on the faces of the people was different. They seemed happier and more carefree. I enjoyed our stop there.

DURING all these tours I took care to use enough prolongations that my companions on the tour could not but

196

note that my speech was different from the speech of others. Also, from time to time I called attention to my prolongations and made it clear that I had a speech problem.

CHAPTER 16

THE SADDEST TIMES

IT SEEMS I had always taken for granted my family's love, devotion and presence, along with the assurance that they wanted me at home whenever it was possible. The summer of 1942 I knew my mother was becoming a bit frail and that she was not as active as at earlier times, but the thought that her condition might be serious seems not to have entered my mind. That autumn her condition became critical. I was home for a few weeks to help take care of her; I was so deeply affected, so distraught, I could not teach while she was so ill. At Thanksgiving time my mother passed away of cancer. That was the first break in our family of four, the first deep sorrow that had come to me. I had been at Racine for three and a half years, so I think my mother could feel assured that my stutter was under sufficient control that my professional life would continue.

Back in Racine during the months that followed I was deeply saddened and lonely. I happened to see a close-out sign on some lovely German-made wool yarn. It was mothproofed and in various colors. I bought quite a supply of that very special yarn and began to knit squares of it for an afghan. The Second World War was on so the store could get no more of that yarn. During the First World War my mother and I knitted sweaters for the soldiers. During that activity of my hands, as my fingers knitted, my thoughts and sorrows seemed someway to become involved with the stitches. That activity brought a degree of peace and quiet to my consciousness and some order to my sorrowing thoughts. Eventually the blocks were put together into a lovely, colorful, serviceable afghan. *At critical times in my life there seems to have been constructive thinking as to how I might save myself.*

After mother was gone father and Harold lived on in the Phillipsburg home. Father did fairly well with the cooking. He learned to bake bread, even to make cakes. I was home with them every summer and at Christmas time as I had always been.

During our sod-house years my parents worried that Harold or I might get infantile paralysis, commonly called polio. Some children died from that. Harold became a Western Union operator, but when he was twenty-two he had polio. His legs were paralyzed. Eventually he learned to walk with crutches and to drive his car. For some years he had a small gas station. Father helped him some and it made an occupation for Harold.

In 1962 I was home for a short time before my trip to Russia. Again I was not very observant for I did not realize Harold was not as well as usual, or I would not have gone on the tour. On my return to Phillipsburg Harold was critically ill. In late August he died from cancer of the liver. (It seems it may be significant that

200

Mother's one nephew, Norman Howe, died of cancer of the liver.) My father was heart broken; it was a time of great sorrow and trial for us both.

After Harold had polio, the plan was firmly in my mind, although I did not talk about it, that when I was retired, he and I would live together. We would live where it was good for him—a mild climate. In addition to the time Harold drove to Aberdeen for me and we saw the Black Hills, we took several summer car trips together, each a week or ten days.

That autumn of 1962 father and I decided he would return to Racine with me, and make that his home thereafter. He had visited me several times in Racine, so he knew the city a little. He had made a few friends there. Mr. Madsen, who was born in Denmark, became a staunch friend.

When I was sixteen my father taught me to drive our new Model T Ford. In Racine I had considered getting a car, but a car did not seem essential and I could scarcely afford one. However I did take some driving lessons and I had a valid driver's license. We decided I should take over Harold's car, a 1955, 88 Oldsmobile. So father and I closed the Phillipsburg house, and we drove back to Racine. We took four days to drive the nine hundred miles for I was not accustomed to driving. Mrs. Moe, my very kind landlady, made father welcome. I gave him my bed and I slept on the davenport.

Father loved the outdoors. In nice weather if I was gone he walked the short distance to one of the small parks nearby. It was only four short blocks to Lake Michigan. Over the next few years we picnicked many times in seasonable weather. We kept charcoal in the car, so it was a simple matter to stop at the meat market for some steak to broil in the woods. Many week-end days we went riding. We would take a picnic lunch and fully enjoy the beauty of the parks and byways. In spring there are many wild flowers in the parks, in autumn the colors are lavish near Lake Michigan. What a blessing that Oldsmobile was for us.

Every summer we drove back to Phillipsburg to see about things there. Harold had a dog, a cocker spaniel. Spotty went everywhere in the car with Harold. When he honked she came at top speed. Dr. Mary, my high school chum, was Harold's doctor. While Harold was so ill, Mary, out of the kindness of her heart, took Spotty. The summer following Harold's illness and death, we were driving very slowly along the main street of Phillipsburg when suddenly a dog was barking and jumping up on the side of the car. Father opened the door and Spotty jumped in. She had recognized the sound of Harold's car. I almost wept. She knew father and me, but we could not have her in Racine.

Father wanted to see the Black Hills. Dr. Madison, our excellent Milwaukee doctor, thought it was all right for father to go, so the next summer, after our trip to Phillipsburg we drove through Nebraska to western South Dakota. We spent one full day driving all through the Black Hills. Mount Rushmore was completed by that time. How we both did enjoy that trip. Those were golden years for both father and me. I came to know him as I never had before.

ONE OF THE SORROWS of my life is that I never knew my mother as well. Three summers we drove to Connecticut where father stayed with his youngest sister while I went abroad on a tour. I felt the need for getting away for a complete change for a few weeks.

At that time in Wisconsin, as in most of the states, when a teacher reached the age of sixty-five he was automatically retired, and so the spring of 1967 I was retired from the Racine school system. But I was not ready psychologically or financially to quit teaching, so I got a position as speech therapist for the western half of Racine County. From Racine I could drive each day to whichever school I was scheduled, thus father's and my life could go on much as when I taught in Racine.

That spring of 1967 my father was not quite so well as he had been, so we planned to spend the summer in Racine. We had an air-conditioner for our small upstairs apartment so we could be comfortable, and Racine on Lake Michigan is a lovely spot at any season of the year. As soon as school was out we drove to Kansas to look after things there, then we settled down to enjoy the summer in Racine. Every day we were out for rides or picnics or to buy vegetables from road-side stands in the country.

Toward autumn father needed prostate surgery; the prostate proved to be malignant. Father was in Columbia Hospital in Milwaukee and then in a good nursing home there for a few weeks. Dr. Madison who had been my doctor for many years looked after father. By Thanksgiving father was able to be home with me in Racine. We hired a practical nurse to be with father while I was away at school, and I took care of him weekends and at night. Father's good friend, Mr. Madsen, came often to visit with him. Father passed away the spring of 1968, two months after his 94th birthday. I was practical about things and seemed to make an adequate adjustment. I was lonely but busy. Evenings I sat in the bedroom where father had been instead of in the living room.

I had intended to spend the summer in Racine, but acquaintances in England invited me to visit them in their seventeenth century home at Clevedon, near Bristol. A Freeway was being put in close to the house, so in a few months the Suttons would be moving to a *new* house, built in 1812. Note the date is 1812 not 1912. I made a quick decision and flew over. It was certainly an experience to be with the Suttons and their three children, and to meet some of their English friends. Tony was a teacher in what corresponds to our high school.

My mother was proud of our bit of Welsh blood. The best way to see Wales seemed to be to rent a car. I needed an automatic-shift car so one had to be driven out from London for me. The Suttons helped me get the car from Bristol, then I drove by myself for a week around Wales. You know in the British Isles cars are driven on the opposite side of the road from the way we drive, so I had constantly to keep in mind which part of the road I should be on. Each evening I made a reservation ahead for the following night. I was quite charmed by the small village of St. David's and the great St. David's Cathedral so I spent an entire day there. St. David's is at the southwest tip of Wales.

THE WINTER of 1968-69 I taught speech therapy in Algoma and in some nearby schools. Algoma is 130 miles north of Racine. I rented a dream-house in Algoma on the shore of Lake Michigan, the house only a stone's throw up from the water of the lake. Every evening I had a wood fire in the fireplace; the big picture window gave a view of which I never tired. I often thought how much my father would have enjoyed living there with me, and how happy I would have been to have him there. One still, cold evening there was a continuous murmur from the lake; the next morning silence—the lake was frozen over. Most weekends I drove back to my apartment in Racine. Algoma is an interesting town, but I missed the feel, the stir of a city—and my friends.

That summer I joined a Special Education Study Group. We were stationed in Lunt in the south of Sweden for four weeks. I got double pneumonia and spent three weeks in a Jewish Hospital in Amsterdam. When I saw Dr. Madison in Milwaukee he said, "Well, you survived that." It was several weeks after my return before Dr. Madison felt I was really well.

So I was a retired person. I arranged for my social security checks to start coming, and I applied for my teacher's pension.

Winters in Kansas are milder than in Wisconsin, so I decided to drive back to my parents' old home in Phillipsburg and spend the cold months of 1969-70 there. It was lonely there but it was also good to be back in the area where my early years were spent. One cousin still lived there, so in fine weather she and I would ride out past the farm I had loved so much and to other interesting nearby places. I renewed acquaintance with some of my school-day friends. Early the spring of 1970 I signed up for a Tour of Spain with Study Abroad and began to read the history of Spain and some of the Spanish literature.

I lingered in Phillipsburg for the fiftieth anniversary of my high school class. The next moring, Memorial Day,

I decorated the graves of my family with peonies my father had planted in the yard of the old home, and began the car trip back to Wisconsin.

The beginning of the Spanish tour was a week in Morocco. That was like being in a different world; but, interesting and enjoyable as that was, I was glad to leave before any of our group got sick there. In Segovia we saw the great Roman Aqueduct which dates from the Roman occupation of Spain, around 300 A.D. This aqueduct is elevated so one gets a spectacular view of it from any location in Segovia. The Arab occuaption, which lasted for 700 years, enriched Spain through the learning and art left behind when the Arabs were driven out in 1492, the year the Spanish discovered America. The trip through Spain was something like a tour through magic-land. As our bus drew up to Granada, gypsy children held out their hands for coins; but then a little later we were in the Alhambra, amid a paradise of delicate, glowing colors. Especially in the Court of the Lions there is a wealth of exquisitely carved stucco. Another important point about Spain is that it has more fine, old tapestries than any of the other countries. Our visit to the Altamira Cave was especially interesting for me since I had seen the Lascaux Cave on the Tour of France.

Spanish food is excellent, varied and interesting, but at one time practically everyone on the tour was more or less ill with diarrhea, even the excellent assistant tour conductor, a Spaniard.

This was one of my most enjoyable trips abroad. After my rather lonely winter in western Kansas, I thoroughly enjoyed the friendly, professional people on the tour.

THE NEXT TWO WINTERS, after a few weeks in Phillipsburg, I drove on to visit a cousin in California near Los Angeles. I simply fell in love with the California climate and put in my application for an apartment in San Diego. I kept writing about the apartment but it seemed there was no vacancy.

Again the autumn of 1972 I drove to Kansas. It must have been a dreary, bleak winter for me. Some of what I felt early that spring comes back to me, but then I did not even try to express in words my emotional state, my feelings. It is only now fourteen years later that I am trying to express in words what my innermost feeling was then. I was lonely. Perhaps I was again the lonely little girl of the prairies. Even in my early thirties when I was confronted with my stuttering and realized how it was blocking my future, I had not experienced the utter desolation and despair I felt that spring of 1973—but then in my thirties I still had my family. It seems the fact that I was alone in the world came home to me in a way it had not before. It was not a matter of financial insecurity. My speech was not affected.

When my parents bought the Phillispburg house some fifty years earlier, the neighborhood was all right, but the house was not in the best part of town. By 1973 the neighborhood had definitely changed; however, I think I could never have lived happily alone in that town after my more than thirty years in Racine.

In early March I began to have severe diarrhea. Boiled milk and dry toast had no positive effect, so after some two weeks I packed the car and drove back to Racine. That was the only way to escape from an environment which I was powerless to change and to which I could not adjust. It seems it was my entire body that panicked so my gastrointestinal tract could not function normally. After nearly two weeks of observation and study of my case at Columbia Hospital in Milwaukee, Dr. Madison mentioned, in a way that seemed casual, that it might be a psychosomatic condition, for the doctors did not find much wrong with me. Nearly twenty years before that Dr. Madison had said I had a condition known as "Spastic colitis." The medical dictionary states: "Spastic colitis is a common condition in which recurrent abdominal pain with constipation and or diarrhea continues for years without any general deterioration in health. There is no detectable structural disease; the symptoms are caused by abnormal muscular contractions in the colon. The cause is unknown, but the condition is often associated with stress or anxiety and may follow a severe infection of the intestines."

I had read enough of Dr. Sigmund Freud's writing to understand a little what the term psychosomatic might indicate, but then in 1973 that diagnosis seemed altogether foreign to me. Dr. Blanton could have helped me but he was no longer living. Some people had nervous breakdowns, but I did not, so I thought. It was not until I was well into this autobiographical study that I fully realized Dr. Madison may have been in part correct in his diagnosis. But now in my late eighties I am again plagued with diarrhea. Finally I discover I no longer tolerate as much milk as I had been drinking. In chapter one I mention my excessive crying for the first nine months of my life. It may be my intolerance for milk was the cause of that crying.

Lomotil, an anti-spasmodic drug, was the only medication that really helped to control the diarrhea. It may be that, even in his earliest months of life, the individual who will become a stutterer is a bit more susceptible, a little more vulnerable to the stress of anxiety, than others; that he reacts more sensitively to his environment; that his body is somewhat more fragile.

Back in my apartment in Racine, that spring of 1973, I again became interested in the daily routine of meals, some housework, study and social life. As I settled into this secure, safe routine the diarrhea became much less bothersome. I made a conscious effort to be as calm and relaxed as possible about everything.

In July I was notified there was an apartment for me in San Diego, so I sent rent money, and I commenced packing my things preparatory to the move. It was October of 1973 before I finally reached San Diego and began to get settled in my new home.

CHAPTER 17

MY MOTHER'S PRAYERS

M Y NEW HOME in San Diego is in a senior-citizen housing complex six miles by birdwing from the Pacific. There are some 500 apartments scattered over 76 acres of rolling hills with a canyon on each side. This low-density population gives a rather luxurious feeling for the area, and makes it pleasant to take walks. At any hour of the day there are some out walking for pleasure and to please their doctors.

A rose bush in the yard. That seems the first thing I observed about my apartment. Now my eleven rose bushes bloom nine months of the year. My favorites are Perfume Delight and Peace. My table seems bare without a rose in a choice vase.

My huge gardenia bush has blooms from June into August, or even September if the weather is hot. When I have gardenias I take three or four to church to share with older persons who do not have a yard. All winter cyclamen plants thrive at my north entrance. I prefer the mini-bloom cyclamen which have a most elusive and delightful fragrance. In April my redwood fuchsia baskets are filled with fresh potting soil and new plants. Swing-time, Vienna Waltz, First Love and Wood Violet are among my choice varieties. The big bougainvillea on a trellis at my bed-room window has red blooms most of the year. Also there is the flaming-orange, flowering ice plant in my yard.

Then there are the birds. The Anna's Hummingbird, the only hummingbird in the United States that sings, is in this area. The house finches regularly nest in the eaves over my terrace. One year a pair made a nest in one corner of one of my fuchsia baskets. I watered that basket from the opposite corner, and in about four weeks four fine, young birds flew across to the nearby bank.

FOR MORE THAN twenty years "Sunrise Semester" was a regular early morning feature on CBS television. Some stations might air it as early as 5:30 a.m., others as late as 6:30 a.m. Whenever there was a literary course I would get up early for those lectures.

The first series of Sunrise Semester lectures that I followed was on Russian Literature. There were two different courses on Contemporary French Literature. The summer of 1980 the Sunrise Semester subject was Contemporary Hispanic Fiction. St. John's University, Jamaica, N.Y., provided the lectures. The booklet from St. John's stated: "The series will provide in-depth discussion of novels written in Spain and in Spanish-speaking Latin American countries from 1945 to the present. These works are responsible for the rebirth in Hispanic letters and have placed Spain and Latin America in the forefront of western contemporary fiction." So I read the fiction of Miguel

Angel Asturias, Gabriel Garcia Márquez, Julio Cortázar, Manuel Puig. I read Mexico's Carlos Fuentes, Peru's Mario Vargas Llosa. Also the poet Pablo Neruda. Then I offered to give a review of Current Hispanic Fiction for the Book Section of A.A.U.W. here in San Diego.

This book review was quite different from the one I gave for A.A.U.W. after I had been in Racine for some years. I began by saying "You know I have a speech problem. With your approval I will work on it a bit as I give this review." And so I used some prolongations. It seems to me that each time I speak of my stutter to people and demonstrate my prolongations it is a decided benefit for me.

NOW IN LATE SEPTEMBER, 1988, I just brought in a fine gardenia hidden inside my huge bush. My roses are full of buds, some showing color. The people at Cadillac keep my 45,000 mile, eleven year old Delta 88 Oldsmobile in perfect condition. I feel a deep abiding peace living here in this year-round climate, in this peaceful area of San Diego away from the rush and crime of the inner city. I feel something of the tranquility of the hot summer evenings of my childhood when at twilight time my family sat out on the north side of our sod house with that vast starry expanse above. My two pension checks, social security and teacher's retirement, plus my account at Prudential Bache fill me with peace and an overwhelming gratitude for the way a magnificent providence has provided for that lonely little child of the prairie.

THE ANSWER to the question "How did the improvement in my speech come about?" lies in a second question.

213

"How did it come about that I made the choices that could really help me?" How did it happen that I chose to work with Dr. Blanton the summer of 1932? I feel certain that without my work with Dr. Blanton I could not have accomplished all I did for my speech and in my work as a speech therapist. After the choice to go to Dr. Blanton's Summer School, and after I knew a little about the American Speech and Hearing Association, it was a normal choice to go to Iowa. "How did I happen to choose the Prolongation Pattern?" Perhaps most of all the question how I happened to mark the stuttered words and the prolongations on which there was no stuttering the summer of 1936—that is, to most carefully discriminate between prolongations with no stuttering and prolongations on which I felt stuttering. *That discrimination, it now seems to me, is what really helped me most of all.*

My mother was a deeply religious person. I feel certain she prayed about my stuttering. Prayers are answered in surprising ways. Perhaps the answer to her prayers was in that I was helped to make the choices that would result in practically perfect speech for me.

214

PAGE FOR STUTTERERS

Resolve: Chapter 10, p. 119 last three lines.

Sensation of stuttering:
 Preface p. xviii
 Chapter 12, Bottom, p. 141.
 Chapter 13, p. 156.

Memory of reciting poems with perfect speech before
my bedroom mirror.
 Chapter 6, p. 69.

What helped me:
 Chapter 13, pp. 153–6; and all italicized lines in
book.

By Chapters:
 Chapter 1, pp. 3–5.
 Chapter 4, pp. 37–39.
 Much of Chapters 6 through 12.
 All of Chapters 13, 14 and 17.

CHRONOLOGY

1901, August 16 . . Born in northwestern Kansas.
1902, Spring . . . . . My parents moved to a new two-room sod house.
1906, January 9 . . My brother, Harold, born.
1908, September My mother began teaching me at home.
1910, Spring . . . . . Halley's Comet.
1910, September . . Entered rural school, third grade.
1914, March 1 . . . . Father bought the Grandpa farm and we moved into a six-room house.
1916, September . . Enrolled in the Phillipsburg High School.
1920, Spring . . . . . The Declamatory Contest.
1920, May . . . . Graduated from the Phillipsburg High School as Salutatorian.
1920-21, Winter . . Taught Silver Light rural school, a seven month term.
1921-23, Winters Taught Pleasant College rural school, seven month terms.
1923-25, Winters Attended the University of Nebraska.

1925-27, Winters   Taught English in the high school at Imperial, Nebraska.

1927-28, Winter . . Attended the University of Nebraska.

1928, June . . . . Granted an A.B. Degree.

1928-29, Winter . . Taught English in the high school at Fairmont, Nebraska.

1929-31, Winters- Taught English Literature in the
Summers . . . . . . Teachers College at Aberdeen, South Dakota.

1931, Spring . . . . . Consulted Dr. Lee Travis at Iowa City.

1931-32, Winter . . Worked toward a Master's Degree in English Literature at the University of Nebraska.

1932, Summer . . . Attended Dr. Smiley Blanton's Speech Summer School at Williamstown, Massachusetts.

1932-33, Winter . . Taught in high school at Long Island, Kansas.

1933, Summer . . . Worked at Dr. Blanton's Speech Summer School.

1933-34, Winter . . Continued work on my Master's Degree at the University of Nebraska.

1934, June . . . . Granted a Master's Degree in English Literature, University of Nebraska.

1934, Summer . . . Worked at Dr. Blanton's Speech Summer School.

1934-35, Winter . . Studied psychology and German at the University of Nebraska, and read English papers.

1935-37, Winters   Studied psychology and speech pathology at the University of Iowa at Iowa City.

1935, December . . Met Dr. Charles Van Riper.

1936, Summer . . . Read aloud every afternoon before my parents.

1936, Autumn . . . Course in Relaxation with Dr. Bagchi.

1937, June . . . . Transferred to the University of Wisconsin at Madison.

1937, September. . Assigned a clinic stutterer to work with.

1938, January . . . . Went to Racine, Wisconsin, to teach speech therapy in the public schools.

1941, June . . . . Surgery for gall stones at Columbia Hospital, Milwaukee.

1942, Autumn . . . Home in Kansas two months to be with my mother, ill with cancer.

1954, Summer . . . My first trip to California.

1956, Summer . . . Attended summer session at Stanford University.

1958 and 1959,
   June . . . . Two weeks at Audubon Camp in Maine.

1960, Summer . . . Six weeks Tour of Latin America.

1961, Summer . . . Study in Paris and Tour of France, six weeks.

1962, Summer . . . Six weeks Seminar in Russia.

1962, August . . . . My brother died of cancer of the liver.

218

1962, September   My father came to live with me in Racine. I took over my brother's Oldsmobile.

1963, Summer . . . Four-weeks Bird Study Tour of Scandinavia, and four-week Study Tour of Greece.

1964, Summer . . . Six weeks National Education Association Exchange Tour of Germany.

1965, Summer . . . Study Tour of England, six weeks.

1966, Summer . . . Second Seminar in Russia, six weeks.

1967, June . . . . Was retired from Racine Public Schools.

1967-68, Winter . . Taught Speech Therapy in the west half of Racine County.

1968, March . . . . . My father passed away at age 94.

1968, Summer . . . Trip to England. Entertained ten days in an English home. Rented a car and drove around Wales.

1968-69, Winter . . Taught speech therapy at Algoma, Wisconsin. Rented a cottage overlooking Lake Michigan.

1969, June . . . . Retired from teaching. Arranged for my Teachers' Pension and Social Security.

1969, Summer . . . Four Week Study Group at Lunt, Sweden.

1969, August . . . . Pneumonia in Amsterdam at a Jewish Hospital.

1969-70, Winter . . In the family home at Phillipsburg, Kansas.